Exploring
EARTH AND SPACE SCIENCE

4

ENE–GON

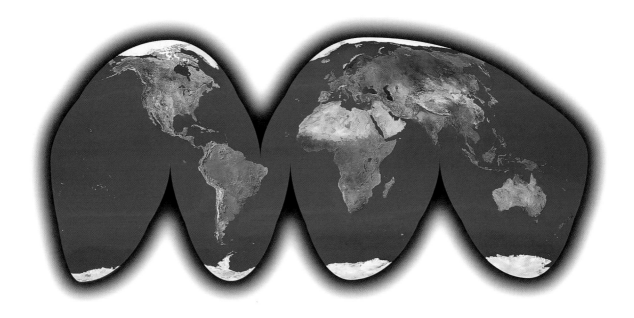

Marshall Cavendish
New York • London • Toronto • Sydney

Marshall Cavendish Corporation
99 White Plains Road
Tarrytown, New York 10591

Website: www.marshallcavendish.com

© 2002 Marshall Cavendish Corporation

Created by **Brown Partworks Limited**

Library of Congress Cataloging-in-Publication Data

Exploring earth and space science.
    p. cm.
    Includes bibliographical references and indexes.
    Contents: 1. Acid and base-Calcium -- 2. Calendar-Continental shelf -- 3. Copper-El
Niño and La Niña -- 4. Energy-Gondwana -- 5. Grassland-Laser -- 6. Light-Meteor -- 7.
Meteorology-Ordovician period -- 8. Ore-Prospecting -- 9. Protein-Star -- 10.
Stratosphere-X ray -- 11. Index.
    ISBN 0-7614-7219-3 (set) -- ISBN 0-7614-7220-7 (v. 1) -- ISBN 0-7614-7221-5 (v. 2)
-- ISBN 0-7614-7222-3 (v. 3) -- ISBN 0-7614-7223-1 (v. 4) -- ISBN 0-7614-7224-X (v.
5) -- ISBN 0-7614-7225-8 (v. 6) -- ISBN 0-7614-7226-6 (v. 7) -- ISBN 0-7614-7227-4
(v. 8) -- ISBN 0-7614-7228-2 (v. 9) -- ISBN 0-7614-7229-0 (v. 10) -- ISBN
0-7614-7230-4 (v. 11)
    1. Earth sciences--Encyclopedias. 2. Space sciences--Encyclopedias. 3.
Astronomy--Encyclopedias

QE5 .E96 2002

550'.3--dc21   00-065801
                                                                                    CIP
                                                                                    AC

ISBN 0-7614-7219-3 (set)

ISBN 0-7614-7223-1 (vol. 4)

Printed in Hong Kong

06 05 04 03 02 01 00   5 4 3 2 1

Exploring
EARTH AND SPACE SCIENCE

4

ENE–GON

Marshall Cavendish
New York • London • Toronto • Sydney

Energy

The capacity of an object to do work

Everyone knows what it means to have energy. When people feel energetic, they can climb mountains, go swimming, or do hard work. Objects that have energy can also do things. A battery full of stored energy can make a flashlight shine for several hours. A drift of snow can fall down a mountain and become a fast-moving avalanche. A rushing river can turn a huge wheel called a turbine and so generate electricity in a hydroelectric power plant.

Scientists have a formal way of defining energy. They say that energy is the capacity to do work and that work involves exerting a force over a distance.

To lift a heavy box, for example, someone must push upward against the force of gravity for the distance they want to lift the box. The work

Electrical energy is generated in hydroelectric power stations by piping water into turbines.

HIGHLIGHTS

- ◆ Scientists define energy as the work that an object can do; work is carried out by a force moving over a distance.

- ◆ Energy cannot be created or destroyed; it can only be changed from one form to another.

- ◆ The main kinds of energy are potential energy (stored energy), kinetic energy (energy of movement), and internal energy (heat).

- ◆ The laws of thermodynamics (heat in motion) explain which types of energy change can and cannot occur.

- ◆ All energy of movement eventually becomes heat.

carried out is equal to the force multiplied by the distance, and it is exactly equal to the energy used in the process.

Where energy comes from

Almost all the energy on Earth comes from the Sun. Sunlight makes plants grow. These plants are eaten by animals and people, who digest them and turn them into useful energy. Over millions of years, fossilized (preserved) plants turn into fuels such as coal, peat, oil, and gas. These fossil fuels can also be used to make energy. The Sun provides heat as well as light. The Sun's heat evaporates water from the sea. When it cools in the atmosphere, it falls as rain. The rain flows into rivers, which have long been used as a source of power in waterwheels and hydroelectric power plants. The Sun's heat also drives the wind, which pushes the ocean waves. Both the wind and waves provide useful energy.

A power plant might generate electricity (electrical energy) by burning lumps of coal that have been mined from the ground, for example. So although the power plant appears to create energy, it is really simply turning energy from one form into another. The same is true of any process in the Universe that starts with one form of energy and ends with another.

Heating a pan of soup on the stove is another example of energy conversion. The heat in the soup is supplied by the burner on the stovetop. The stove itself might get its heat from electricity. This in turn comes from a power plant, which may perhaps get its energy by taking energy from a fast-moving river.

One very important law of physics is that energy can never be created or destroyed, only changed from one form into another. This law is called the conservation of energy. It is at the center of everything that happens in the Universe. It explains why cars need fuel, why people must eat, and why engineers have never managed to build a perpetual motion machine (one that runs forever without stopping).

Potential energy

A snowboarder standing on top of a mountain appears to have no energy. He is just standing there. As he starts moving, however, he picks up

LOOK CLOSER

Storing Energy

People do not always want to use energy at exactly the moment or in exactly the place that it is produced. There are numerous ways of storing potential energy for later use. Night storage heaters have large bricks inside them. At night, when electricity is cheap, the bricks are heated up. The bricks release this stored heat very slowly throughout the day. Hydroelectric power plants also use electricity in this way. At night they use cheap electricity to pump water up into a high dam. The water is then released during the day to produce electricity at times when demand is at its greatest.

speed and may be traveling very fast by the time he reaches the bottom. Has energy been created from nowhere?

The snowboarder did have a type of hidden energy at the top of the mountain. This energy is called potential energy because it gives people and objects the potential (or capacity) to do work. When the snowboarder climbed the mountain he did some work by moving his body weight against the downward force of gravity. He used energy that his body had made from food to do this. As the law of conservation of energy says, energy does not simply disappear into thin air. The energy in the food is used to climb the mountain. This climbing gives the snowboarder an equal amount of energy that he can use in other ways. Potential energy can always be stored and used later.

Climbing a mountain is not the only way to store potential energy. Winding a clock stores potential energy in a spring. This energy is gradually released to keep the clock ticking. Charging a battery by passing an electric current through it creates electrical potential energy. This form of energy can be released later when the battery is used to power an object such as a flashlight or a cassette player.

Pulling back the elastic of a catapult also stores potential energy in the stretchy elastic. When the elastic is released, the energy fires a missile at great speed.

Inside a light bulb, electrical energy is converted into light energy and heat energy.

Gradually, the kinetic energy the bungee jumper had when she was moving is changed back into potential energy stored in the stretched bungee cord. When she stops moving downward, the cord pulls her back up again and starts her moving upward. The potential energy stored in the cord is then changed into kinetic energy again.

Why does the bungee jumper not bounce right back up to the top of the bridge and keep on bouncing up and down forever? The conservation of energy law seems to suggest this is exactly what should happen because the jumper's original potential energy should be restored when the bungee cord springs her back upward. However, no process that changes energy from one form to any other is ever quite perfect. Some energy is always lost in the form of heat. The bungee jumper loses some energy as she falls because air resistance pushes against her body and the air around her warms a bit. The bungee cord also loses some energy every time it is stretched because it too warms up slightly and loses energy as heat. These energy losses gradually use up all the original potential energy, which slows down the jumper and eventually brings her movement to a halt.

Heat and internal energy

The bungee cord is not the only thing that eventually turns all its energy into heat. All energy of motion eventually becomes heat. When a car driver brakes, for example, brake pads are applied to the wheels, and they slow the car by changing its kinetic energy into heat. It is the friction between the brake pad and the wheels that produces this heat. This explains why the brakes on a bicycle get hot if you slow down very quickly by braking hard. Where does the energy go when something becomes hot, and how is the heat stored? The molecules (atoms bonded together) in a substance such as rubber are constantly moving around. This is a type of kinetic energy, but because it is hidden inside the

Kinetic energy

Stored potential energy can be changed rapidly into a number of other forms of energy. One of the most important of these energy forms is kinetic energy, or the energy that something has because it is moving. When a bungee jumper leaps from a high bridge, for example, she has a great deal of potential energy at the beginning. As gravity pulls her toward Earth, she moves faster and faster.

Eventually, all the potential energy she originally had is changed into kinetic energy. At the bottom, however, the bungee cord begins to stretch again and the jumper starts to slow down.

rubber, it is usually called internal energy. When rubber is heated, the molecules move around more quickly. The rubber is hotter, which means its molecules are moving more quickly than they did before.

Hot objects can also transfer their heat to colder objects. When a pan full of cold soup is placed on top of a hot stove, heat transfers from the stove to the soup and warms it. Three different processes, called conduction, convection, and radiation, are involved in heating the soup. Because the hot stove is in contact with the cold pan, heat transfers by conduction. Heat passes from one object to another simply because they are touching. The soup at the bottom of the pan is much closer to the stove than the soup at the top. This warm soup rises in the pan. As it rises, the warm soup meets colder soup, begins to cool, and falls down again. Gradually, all the soup rises and falls like a slowed-down fountain. This process, called convection, eventually warms all the soup in the pan. Convection explains how heat transfers through gases (such as air above a heater) or liquids (such as soup).

Another heat transfer process is also at work. Just as a light bulb or a radiator gives off heat, so the hot pan of soup gives off heat to its surroundings by a process called radiation. When the stove is turned off, radiation causes the soup gradually to become cold.

Energy conversion

Energy can be changed in all sorts of different ways. Chemical potential energy in a battery can make a light bulb shine. The potential energy makes an electric current flow through a thin metal wire called a filament and so produces both light and heat.

Any device that converts (changes) energy from one form to another is called a transducer. An electric motor is a transducer because it converts electrical energy into mechanical energy that makes the axle of the motor spin around. Other examples of transducers include microphones (which convert sound energy into electrical energy), loudspeakers (which convert electrical energy into sound energy), solar panels (which convert sunlight into electrical energy or heat), and LEDs (light-emitting diodes, which convert electrical energy into light).

LOOK CLOSER

Swing Energy

A girl riding on a swing constantly changes potential energy into kinetic energy and back again. At the top of the swing, for an instant the girl is not moving. She has lots of potential energy but no kinetic energy. As she starts to swing, her potential energy is gradually converted into kinetic energy, which gives her speed. At the bottom of the swing, she has a great deal of kinetic energy. When the swing climbs again, the kinetic energy is gradually converted back into potential energy.

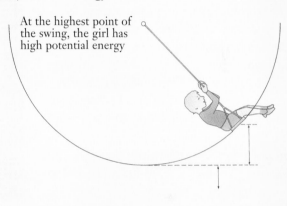

At the highest point of the swing, the girl has high potential energy

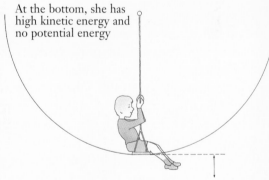

At the bottom, she has high kinetic energy and no potential energy

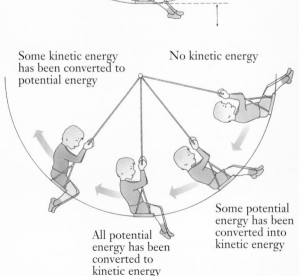

Some kinetic energy has been converted to potential energy

No kinetic energy

All potential energy has been converted to kinetic energy

Some potential energy has been converted into kinetic energy

DISCOVERERS

James Prescott Joule

English physicist James Prescott Joule (1818–1889) carried out a famous experiment to prove that different kinds of energy are the same thing. He fitted a large paddle wheel inside a sealed metal cylinder filled with water and made the wheel turn around by connecting it to a heavy falling weight. The weight originally had potential energy. As it fell, this potential energy was changed into kinetic energy in the paddle wheel. As the paddle wheel spun around, it stirred the water vigorously and warmed the water very slightly.

Joule proved that the amount of energy causing the water to warm was exactly the same as the potential energy that the weight had had to begin with. In this way Joule demonstrated what he called "the mechanical equivalent of heat" and what is today called the conservation of energy.

However, there are some restrictions on how energy can be converted. The conservation of energy law states that the total amount of energy before a particular change takes place is exactly the same as the total amount of energy afterward. When a pan of soup is heated, the total energy produced by the stove is equal to the extra internal energy (heat) gained by the soup, in addition to the energy that the soup loses to the surroundings by radiation, as well as any other energy losses that may occur. This is an example of the first law of thermodynamics (the science of heat in motion).

Another important law called the second law of thermodynamics states that some types of energy conversion simply never happen. When the pan of soup is left on the stove, it gradually loses its energy to the kitchen. The soup cools down quite a lot, and the kitchen warms up very slightly. However, the reverse of this never happens. If the soup is cold, then it never sucks energy from the kitchen to warm itself up and make the kitchen cooler. The second law of thermodynamics is another way of saying that heat does not flow from a cooler object to a warmer one, it only flows from a warm object to a cold one.

German-born U.S. scientist Albert Einstein (1879–1955) changed the world forever when he discovered another remarkable method of converting energy. In 1905 he explained that energy and matter (which is also called mass) are actually the same thing and that a very small amount of matter can be converted into a huge amount of energy. This discovery helped scientists to understand how energy can be produced by the process of nuclear fission (FIH-shuhn; where large atoms are broken into smaller ones) and nuclear fusion (FYOO-zhuhn; where small atoms are joined to make larger ones) and led to the development of nuclear power and nuclear weapons.

CHECK THESE OUT!
✔ELASTICITY ✔ELECTRICITY ✔HEAT
✔MOMENTUM ✔THERMODYNAMICS

Equinox and Solstice

Equinox marks the beginning of spring and autumn; solstice marks the beginning of summer and winter

In the Northern Hemisphere (the top half of Earth from the Arctic to the equator, the imaginary line that divides Earth in two), the longest day falls on June 21 or 22. This is the day when the Sun shines the longest in the sky, and it is called the summer solstice (SOHLZ-tihs; from the Latin *solstitium*, meaning "Sun stands still"). The summer solstice is officially the beginning of summer. Winter begins at the winter solstice, on December 21 or 22, which is the shortest day.

The central stone of the Ballachroy standing stones in Scotland points to where the Sun set at the summer solstice in 1800 B.C.E. This would have been the right-hand peak of the central mountain.

HIGHLIGHTS

◆ The spring and autumn equinoxes are the dates when the noon Sun is directly overhead at Earth's equator, and day and night are of equal length.

◆ Solstices are the dates when—in the Northern Hemisphere—the noon Sun is highest in the sky in summer, and lowest in the sky in winter.

◆ Through the year, the Sun appears to move along a great circle against the background of the stars. This path is called the ecliptic.

◆ The stars can be imagined as fixed on the inside of a huge sphere that turns about Earth, called the celestial sphere. The celestial sphere has an equator equivalent to Earth's equator.

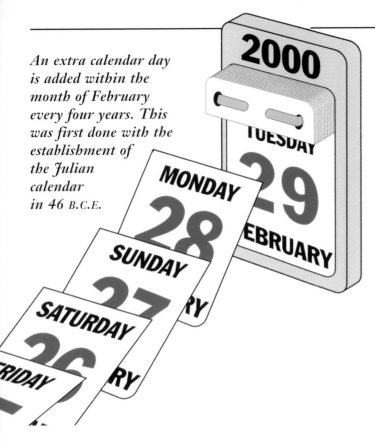

Halfway between the summer and winter solstices, the Sun at noon is directly overhead at the equator, and day and night are equal in length all over the world. These days are called the spring and autumn equinoxes (EE-kwuh-NAHKS-suhz; from the Latin *equinoxium*, meaning "equal night"). They fall around March 21 and September 22. The March equinox marks the beginning of spring, and the September equinox marks the beginning of autumn.

The solstices and equinoxes do not always fall on the usual dates because a year is actually nearly a quarter of a day longer than 365 days. The calendar corrects for this by adding one full day every leap year. Some special rules apply to years divisible by 100. In those years, the leap year day is not observed unless the year is also divisible by 400. Even so, the calendar can be out of step with the beginning of the seasons by nearly a day before it is corrected.

The changes through the seasons happen because Earth's axis (the imaginary rod around which it rotates) is tilted. For half the year, the Northern Hemisphere is tilted toward the Sun as Earth moves around it. This is the time of spring and summer. In the other half of the year, the Northern Hemisphere is tilted away from the Sun. This time is fall and winter. Spring and summer in the Southern Hemisphere (the bottom half of Earth from the equator to the Antarctic) occur when it is fall and winter in the Northern Hemisphere. This is because the Northern Hemisphere is tilted away from the Sun when the Southern Hemisphere is tilted toward it, and the other way around.

The ecliptic and the celestial equator

All the stars in the sky can be imagined as if they are on the inside of a huge ball, with Earth at its center. This ball is called the celestial sphere. Although Earth moves around the Sun, it looks as if the Sun moves around Earth in a great circle against the background of the stars. This circle is called the ecliptic. The Sun appears to move east along the ecliptic against the background of the stars. The stars behind the Sun cannot be seen in daytime because the Sun is too bright. The neighboring stars can be seen just before sunrise or just after sunset because the Sun can be located but is not too bright. At those times it is easy to calculate the exact location of the Sun on the ecliptic. Around the celestial sphere, the ecliptic is traced through 12 major constellations (groups of stars). These are called the zodiac (from the Greek, meaning "circle of animals") because many of the constellations, such as Leo and Scorpio, are named after animals.

Because Earth rotates, the celestial sphere seems to turn around Earth once every 24 hours. The axis of the celestial sphere is therefore the same as Earth's axis. Earth's equator can be imagined as having an equivalent celestial equator on the celestial sphere. Because Earth's axis is tilted by about 23 degrees and 30 minutes, the celestial equator is similarly tilted 23 degrees and 30 minutes away from the ecliptic.

At the equinoxes, the ecliptic crosses the celestial equator. From the time of the spring equinox to the time of the summer solstice, the ecliptic moves steadily away from the celestial equator, so the Sun appears higher in the sky at noon each day. The days also get steadily longer until the summer solstice. Then the Sun gradually appears lower, past the autumn equinox, to the winter solstice, and the days get shorter and shorter. After this, the noon Sun gradually rises higher in the sky, and then the days get longer again.

Precession of the equinoxes

By convention, the spring equinox is said to occur at the first point of Aries. This is because, more than 2,000 years ago, the Sun at this time appeared to be entering the constellation of Aries, the Ram. However, it is now located against the background of Pisces, the Fish. Around the year 2100, the Sun will appear to enter the constellation of Aquarius, the Water Bearer. This change is called the precession of the equinoxes.

Precession of the equinoxes happens because, as Earth rotates, it also wobbles, just like a spinning top wobbles as it turns. Because of the wobble, Earth's axis is very slowly tracing a small circle on the celestial sphere. This process takes about 26,000 years. The celestial equator is wobbling in the same way, and the points at which it crosses the ecliptic—the equinoxes—are gradually moving westward through the zodiac. Earth's axis presently points toward the North Star. In about 12,000 years, it will have moved to point toward the bright star Vega.

The explanation for precession was first given by English scientist Sir Isaac Newton (1642–1727). It is caused by the gravitational pull of the Sun and the Moon on Earth. The Moon's gravity also causes Earth's axis to make a very small nodding motion, called nutation, over a period of 18 years and 7 months.

CHECK THESE OUT!
✔CALENDAR ✔CONSTELLATION
✔COSMOLOGY ✔DAY ✔SEASON

STORY OF SCIENCE

Ancient Monuments and Rituals

Ancient people had to know when to plant their crops and when to expect the first winter freeze. Their priests were able to forecast the time of the seasons by studying the movement of the Sun in the sky. So the equinoxes and solstices have long been occasions for celebrations and religious festivals. Christians celebrate Christmas close to the winter solstice, and Easter close to the spring equinox. The dates of the equinoxes and solstices can be discovered by watching the point on the horizon where the Sun rises and sets. During the year in the Northern Hemisphere, starting from the spring equinox, the sunrise and sunset points move north until the summer solstice, then south until the winter solstice, then north again. At the equinoxes, the Sun rises and sets due east.

Native Americans used mountains on the horizon as reference points for sunrise and sunset. Where there were no mountains, they sometimes set up poles or stones. Many prehistoric peoples in Europe did the same. The ancient Maya people designed the great pyramid at Chichén Itzá, in Mexico, so that light patterns like serpents seemed to climb up and down its sides at the equinoxes.

The ruined ancient Mayan city of Chichén Itzá was founded in about the 6th century C.E.

Erosion

Erosion is the gradual wearing away of Earth's surface through natural processes. Sometimes these processes are helped by human activities such as clearing areas of land of trees and other plants. The main agents of erosion are water and wind. Rivers, waves, glaciers, and wind all help to break down surface rock and soil and carry away the debris (duh-BREE; broken pieces) that has been loosened. Large quantities of loose rock and soil can also slide or fall away downhill in a process scientists call mass wasting.

Earth's surface is changing all the time. In many parts of the world, the land is being lifted up to form mountains and high plateaus. This process is continually counteracted by erosion. Running water cuts down into hills to create canyons. Sediment (SEH-duh-muhnt; small particles of material) is carried downstream by streams and rivers to be dropped (deposited) in valleys. Along the coast, pounding waves wear away cliffs and beaches. Glaciers scour and scrape the land that they move over. Wind also scours the land and carries away loose rock particles.

The nature of the land surface influences the speed at which erosion takes place. Generally, a hard rock, such as dolerite, is worn away more slowly than rocks such as clay. Climate (an area's regular weather pattern) also has a major influence on erosion. The amount of rain and snow the area receives, the temperature range of the area, and the prevailing winds all contribute toward the speed of erosion. Erosion is usually fastest in steep areas that receive high rainfall. It is slower in flat deserts and cold lowlands. Human activities such as mining and tree-cutting also speed up the process of erosion by exposing soil to water and wind.

Flowing water

Almost all landscapes are changed by flowing water at some time. One of the most spectacular examples of the effects of running water is the Grand Canyon of the Colorado River in the United States. Scientists call the rock-breaking action of flowing water fluvial erosion. Flowing water erodes the land by the force of its motion and by picking up material from the surface over which it flows. Underground streams and rivers can erode the rocks below the surface in a similar way to surface streams. Fragments of rock may be suspended (carried) in the water or they may dissolve in it. In turn, particles of rock in flowing water speed up the process of erosion as they crash against the banks, the streambed, and each other, loosening other pieces of rock.

The force of gravity makes water flow downhill. The steeper the slope, the faster the water flows and the more material it can carry. Sand is easy for water to lift and carry. Coarse gravel is heavier and harder to pick up.

If there is a sudden drop in the land surface over which water flows, a waterfall forms. The falling water speeds up erosion still more. It can drill round potholes in the rock at the base of the waterfall, especially if there are pebbles in the water. As chunks of hard rock break off, so the waterfall moves upstream, and a deep gorge is eroded in a downstream direction.

When sloping land is first exposed to rain, as on hillsides where people have just felled many trees, rainwater spreads out into thin sheets as it

HIGHLIGHTS

- ◆ Erosion is the gradual wearing away of the land by natural forces such as water and wind, as well as by humans and animals.

- ◆ Water is the main force behind erosion. Almost all landscapes have been eroded at some time by flowing water.

- ◆ Deserts are eroded by flowing water, ice, and wind.

- ◆ On hillsides, large quantities of loose, eroded material may slide or slip downhill. This process is called mass wasting.

flows downhill. If the slope is steep, the sheet of water can dislodge fragments of rock. The water seeps into cracks and loosens more material. Small channels form and then deeper channels called rivulets form. Next, little streams form. Gradually, V-shaped valleys develop at the base of the slopes. As erosion continues, the valleys eat into higher ground, effectively moving uphill. Scientists call this process headward erosion.

Where a stream suddenly reaches more level ground, it flows more slowly and deposits the rock particles it is carrying. The material collects and spreads out to form a fan-shaped deposit called an alluvial (uh-LOO-vee-uhl) fan. Where a stream or river flows into a lake or ocean, a fan-shaped delta may form.

When a river enters a wide plain, it starts to take a more winding course. On the outside curves of its channel, the water moves faster and undercuts the bank. On the inside curves, more material is deposited, forming meanders (mee-AHN-duhrz; bends). Over time, the meanders become more and more exaggerated and looping.

Glaciers

Glaciers are extremely powerful forces of erosion. They are slow-flowing masses of ice made as snow becomes compacted (packed-

A period of heavy rain has led to the collapse of this river bank. The river carries so much sediment that the water is colored brown.

down). Glaciers erode the ground they move over. Some glaciers are thousands of feet thick. The bottom-most ice melts under the weight of the ice pressing down on it. This water seeps into surface cracks in the rock where it refreezes. The cracks become wider because the ice takes up more space than the original water. Broken pieces of rock are carried along with the glacier. Materials as fine as silt (which is made of very small particles) and as massive as huge boulders are picked up and carried along. Rock fragments in the ice grind and scour the bedrock they move over, producing scratches and grooves in the rock. Some rocks are ground to fine silt by the moving glacier.

Glaciers exist in both polar and subpolar regions and in high mountains. Mountain glaciers cut deep, steep-sided bowls called cirques (SUHRKS) in the mountains. A horn is a high, sharp peak formed where three or more cirques meet. A notable example is the Matterhorn in Switzerland. Other mountain features carved by glaciers include U-shaped valleys and fjords—deep coastal valleys that have become flooded by the sea to form narrow inlets. Hanging valleys are glacial valleys that join the main valley from the side. They are higher than the main valley. Hanging valleys are found in Yosemite National Park in California.

Wave erosion

Waves whipped up by winds erode coastal cliffs and beaches. They do the most damage during storms. Waves wear away a coastline through their pounding action. They throw pebbles at cliff faces. Waves may also pick up sand and gravel as they churn, which speeds up the pace of erosion by scouring the rock. Great water pressure builds up in the cracks in the rock, and it helps to break up the rocks.

Wave erosion creates many distinctive features on sea coasts. High, sheer cliff faces, arches, and sea stacks are seen along some coasts, such as the chalk cliffs of southern Britain. Headlands that jut out into the sea get the full force of wave action. The waves cut a notch into the base of sea cliffs near the waterline. Eventually the overhanging rock crumbles and falls. Rock fragments are deposited in bays between cliffs. If the rocks are soft near the waterline, sea caves and arches may form. When an arch collapses, a column of rock called a sea stack is left.

Erosion in deserts

Deserts are areas that receive less than 10 inches (25 cm) of rain each year. Dry winds erode desert landscapes, lifting and carrying away silt and sand. There are extensive river systems in many deserts, but they are often dry for many years at a time. Some exceptions include the Nile in Egypt and the Colorado River in the United States. Streams in dry areas usually flow only when it rains. A streambed without water is called a dry wash or a wadi (WAH-dee).

When rain finally arrives, it usually falls heavily in a storm or a cloudburst. The dry ground does not absorb the moisture easily,

Coastal erosion is caused by wind-driven waves. The size of the waves depends on the wind speed. Waves are at their most damaging during storms.

The effects of erosion can be seen in this photograph of Delicate Arch, which is situated in Arches National Park, Utah. Erosion has carved away the middle of one side of the arch.

heavy to be carried high in the air. Instead, it is shifted along near the ground. Extreme wind erosion can create great dust storms. During the 1930s, the Great Plains area of the United States was devastated by violent dust storms.

Second, sand particles carried by the wind can scour and erode the landscape. Wind-carried sand can blast rocky outcrops into pinnacles (narrow, upright formations). Since most of the erosion takes place near ground level, high pinnacles may develop carved, slender bases under precariously balanced tops.

Mass wasting

On hillsides, large quantities of loose, eroded material may slide, slip, or creep downhill. It may happen suddenly or gradually over a long period of time. Scientists call this often dramatic process mass wasting. The steeper the slope, the more likely it is that gravity will cause the earth and rock to move downhill. The nature of the rock, and the amount of water it contains, affect when and where mass wasting takes place. Ground cover is also important. If the soil surface is covered by vegetation, the plant roots will help bind the soil and prevent erosion.

Mass wasting takes different forms, depending on the surrounding conditions. Very slow downhill movement of soil is called soil creep. Mudflows or earthflows occur when heavy rain has fallen in a dry region or on slopes where there is little vegetation. Mudflows can be rapid and very destructive. Earthquakes and volcanoes sometimes trigger dangerous flows of mud and earth in mountainous regions.

Rockslides are another form of mass wasting. They are often triggered by rain or melting snow. When loose soil and rock are carried downhill as a mass, the fall is called a slump. True rockslides occur where large numbers of rocks slide downhill at once.

particularly as it often has very little vegetation. Instead, water pours off the land, leading to erosive flash floods. Very heavy rains may saturate the soil to create a muddy torrent that sends boulders crashing downstream.

Eroded landscapes called badlands are formed by flowing water in dry regions with loose soil. Sharp ridges and deep gullies characterize these landscapes. Badlands can be observed in both North and South Dakota and in Montana in the United States. A striking example of a badlands landscape can be found in the semiarid region of Death Valley, California.

Wind can alter desert landscapes in two ways. First, it can pick up dry, loose dust and carry it long distances. Large deposits of silt called loess (LES), carried by winds, can be found worldwide, but especially in northern Europe. Sand is too

CHECK THESE OUT!

✔CANYON ✔CLIFF ✔CLIMATE ✔DELTA
✔GLACIER ✔GROUNDWATER ✔ICE AGE
✔LIMESTONE ✔MOUNTAIN ✔WAVES

Eurasia

The largest continent (landmass) on Earth is called Eurasia (yoo-RAY-zhuh). It is made up of the land areas of both Europe and Asia, and it covers 21 million square miles (55 million sq km)—more than a third of all Earth's dry land. Modern Eurasia holds more than 70 countries, including Russia, the nations of western Europe, most nations of the Middle East, and Asian countries including Thailand, China, and Japan.

Drifting plates

Earth is made of different layers. The crust (outer layer) is made of several tectonic (tek-TAH-nik) plates—huge slabs of rock that fit together like pieces in a giant jigsaw puzzle. Tectonic plates are made of Earth's crust on the surface and a small part of the upper mantle below. The plates are rigid. They float like huge rafts on the lower mantle.

Tectonic plates may carry both dry land and ocean. Most of modern Eurasia lies on top of the Eurasian plate, which is Earth's largest plate. This plate bears the whole of Europe and Asia,

Iceland is situated on the western edge of the Eurasian plate. Earth's crust is weak here, and Iceland is the site of many volcanoes.

HIGHLIGHTS

◆ Eurasia is made up of the land areas of Europe and Asia.

◆ Most of modern Eurasia lies on the upper part of the Eurasian plate, one of the giant plates that make up the outer layer of Earth.

◆ Where the edges of the Eurasian plate meet with neighboring plates, earthquakes and volcanoes sometimes occur. Millions of years ago, other plates collided with the Eurasian plate to form high mountains such as the Himalayas.

except for the Middle East, India, and the far east of Russia. Earth's tectonic plates drift very slowly, driven by currents in the hot rock deep inside Earth. Plates may collide (push together), grind against one another, or gradually pull apart.

Plate boundaries

In the east, the Eurasian plate borders on the Pacific plate and on the much smaller Philippine plate. Along these boundaries, the plates push

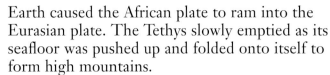

against one another. As they collide, the Pacific and Philippine plates are forced under the Eurasian plate in a process called subduction.

In the south, the Eurasian plate meets the African, Arabian, and Indian-Australian plates. Along much of the border with the African plate, the two plates rub against one another. This rubbing often causes earthquakes. Elsewhere along the southern border, the other plates are slowly being forced under the Eurasian plate.

In the west, the Eurasian plate meets the North American plate roughly halfway across the Atlantic Ocean. These two plates are very slowly drifting apart, which allows molten (liquid) rock from deep inside Earth to well up and erupt on the seabed as lava (LAH-vuh). In the middle of the Atlantic, the lava has built up to form an undersea mountain chain called the Mid-Atlantic Ridge. A deep gash runs down the center of the ridge, marking the boundary between the plates. Scientists have discovered that the Eurasian and North American plates are drifting apart at the rate of roughly 1 inch (2.5 cm) per year.

Mountains of Eurasia

The Ural Mountains divide Eurasia into Europe in the west and Asia in the east. The Alps in south-central Europe are another major mountain chain. They stretch through France, Italy, Switzerland, and Austria, and reach their highest point at Mont Blanc, at 15,771 feet (4,807 m).

The Alps have many spectacular features that were caused by glaciers. The rocks that make up the Alps were formed many millions of years ago in an ancient ocean called the Tethys. During the Mesozoic era (between around 245 million years ago and 66 million years ago), the Tethys lay between the Eurasian and African plates. Later, about 65 million years ago, forces deep inside

Earth caused the African plate to ram into the Eurasian plate. The Tethys slowly emptied as its seafloor was pushed up and folded onto itself to form high mountains.

In Asia, the Himalayas make up the world's highest mountain range. They were also formed by folding, although the process happened more recently, beginning 40 to 60 million years ago. The mountains were created when the Indian plate slowly collided with the Eurasian plate. The edge of the Indian plate was forced down, while lighter sediments from the floor of the Tethys Sea were forced upward to form the Himalayas. Fossils (preserved remains) of ammonites (ancient spiral-shelled sea animals) are still commonly found thousands of feet up in the Himalayas. The highest summit in the Himalayas, Mount Everest, at 29,028 feet (8,848 m) high, is the highest point on Earth.

Volcanoes of Eurasia

Volcanoes often form along the edges of plate boundaries, where Earth's crust is weak enough to allow molten rock from deep inside Earth to erupt onto the surface. There are a number of volcanoes around the western edge of the Eurasian plate, in Iceland and the Azores, an island chain west of Spain. The eastern edge has volcanoes along its whole length, particularly around Japan and the Philippines, where Eurasia borders the Pacific plate.

In past centuries, some of the most dramatic volcanic eruptions in history have taken place along the rim of the Eurasian plate. In 1815, Mount Tambora in Indonesia erupted, throwing huge quantities of ash into the upper atmosphere. The ash partly blocked the Sun's rays from reaching Earth, causing temperatures to drop by about 3.6°F (2°C) around the world. In 1883, Mount Krakatoa, also in Indonesia, erupted. The explosion was heard thousands of miles away. More recently, in 1991, Mount Pinatubo in the Philippines exploded. The eruption killed more than 1,500 people.

CHECK THESE OUT!
✔ATLANTIC OCEAN ✔CONTINENT ✔EARTH ✔EARTHQUAKE ✔GLACIER ✔MESOZOIC ERA ✔PLATE TECTONICS ✔VOLCANO

Evaporation and Boiling

The ways a liquid can change into a gas below or at its boiling point

A bowl of water dries out because it gradually turns into gas. A pan of water boils dry on a stove if it is heated for a long time. The two processes are related. In both cases a liquid turns into a gas. The difference is that the water in the bowl dries well below its boiling point, at room temperature (68°F, or 20°C). A pan of water boils dry at 212°F (100°C), which is the boiling point (boiling temperature) of water.

Vapor pressure

The molecules (MAH-lih-kyoolz; atoms bonded together) in a liquid attract one another with a force that is strong enough to prevent the liquid from breaking up and forming a gas, but not strong enough to make the liquid into a solid. The molecules slip past each other at an average speed that depends on temperature. The higher the temperature, the faster the molecules move. Some molecules move faster than average, however. Some molecules move so fast that they can break free from the liquid if they reach its surface. Because of this effect, the space above a liquid substance will always contain some vapor of that substance. This creates the vapor pressure of that liquid. At higher temperatures, more molecules move fast enough to leave the liquid, so the vapor pressure increases.

Evaporation

In a closed can of paint, molecules of solvent vapor reenter the liquid as often as molecules of liquid escape into the vapor. Because of this two-way traffic of solvent molecules, the paint does not become dry. If the lid of the can is removed, the vapor escapes, and overall more solvent leaves the liquid than reenters it. The paint starts to dry. The surface area of the liquid is an

HIGHLIGHTS

♦ Liquids evaporate more rapidly when they are spread over a large area.

♦ The boiling point is the temperature at which a liquid's vapor pressure matches the air pressure.

♦ Liquids boil at lower temperatures if the pressure is reduced.

important factor in how quickly it evaporates. Paint in an open can has a small surface area, so it dries slowly. Once it is applied to a wall, the same volume of paint has a much larger surface area. The solvent can evaporate much more quickly and the paint dries in a few hours. If a draft passes over the painted surface, it dries even more rapidly. The draft carries away the solvent vapor, which cannot go back into the paint.

Evaporative cooling

A liquid evaporates as its faster-moving molecules escape as vapor. This results in the average speed of molecules in the liquid dropping. A lower speed means that the liquid is cooler. The human body makes use of this cooling effect during sweating. Sweat on the skin evaporates, and the body cools down.

At the boiling point of water, enough of the molecules are moving fast enough for bubbles of vapor to form spontaneously anywhere in the liquid. The bubbles are lighter than the surrounding liquid and rise to the surface. Clouds of steam are produced as the hot vapor escapes from the kettle.

The cooling towers of power stations and air-conditioning plants also use evaporative cooling. Inside the towers, droplets of warm water partially evaporate in a stream of air, leaving the water at a lower temperature. Water droplets have a larger surface area, and the current of air carries away the water vapor. Therefore, the water evaporates and cools more rapidly than it would as a body of water in a tank.

Boiling

Warming a liquid increases its vapor pressure as more molecules escape the liquid. The boiling point of a liquid is the temperature at which its vapor pressure matches the pressure around the liquid. At sea level, the vapor pressure of water reaches atmospheric pressure at 212°F (100°C).

The summit of Mount Everest is 29,028 feet (8,848 m) above sea level. At this altitude, the air pressure is much lower than at sea level. Because of this, the vapor pressure of water matches the air pressure at the lower temperature of 162°F (72°C).

CHECK THESE OUT!
✔GAS ✔HEAT ✔LIQUID
✔MELTING AND BOILING POINTS

EVERYDAY SCIENCE

Distillation

Many industrial processes, such as oil refining, rely on distillation to separate mixtures of liquids. Distillation uses the different vapor pressures of substances to separate them. The mixture will usually begin to boil at a temperature between the boiling points of the pure liquids, and the vapor will contain more of the lower boiling point substance. A piece of equipment called a condenser cools the vapor in another part of the apparatus. As it cools, the vapor becomes a liquid and is collected. This liquid may have to go through several distillations.

Some compounds start to break up before their vapor pressure reaches atmospheric pressure. They can be separated from mixtures if distilled at reduced pressure. The mixture boils at a low enough temperature that the compound will not break up.

Explorer Probe

**A series of NASA satellites
that carry out scientific experiments**

The very first U.S. satellite put into orbit around Earth was *Explorer 1*, launched in 1958. Since then, more than 70 Explorer probes have been launched. A probe is an automatic spacecraft that takes scientific measurements.

Explorer 1 was a small satellite, but it was very important to the young U.S. space program. In the 1950s, the United States and the Soviet Union were involved in a space race. Both wanted to prove that their rocket technology was best because rockets might have to be used to launch nuclear warheads in the event of a war. A rocket is an engine or a vehicle that does not need to take in air to burn its fuel because it carries it own oxidizer aboard.

The Soviet Union launched its first satellite, *Sputnik 1*, on October 4, 1957, while the United States trailed behind. The Vanguard rocket that was going to launch the first U.S. satellite exploded on its launch pad—the newspapers called it "flopnik."

To get a successful satellite launch, the U.S. government now turned to Wernher von Braun (1912–1977), a German-born scientist who had developed rocket technology in Germany during World War II (1939–1945). Using missile technology, he launched a satellite on January 31, 1958. This was *Explorer 1*.

Explorer 1 saved the U.S. space program and sent valuable scientific information from space. A Geiger counter (radiation detector) on board discovered high levels of radiation in belts around Earth. U.S. physicist James Van Allen (born 1914) realized that these radiation belts are high-energy particles from the Sun getting trapped in Earth's magnetic field. Today these radiation belts are named the Van Allen belts.

The Explorer series

Wernher von Braun and his team went on to launch two more Explorers in 1958. Explorer

Explorer 1 was launched by rocket in 1958.

HIGHLIGHTS

◆ *Explorer 1* was the first U.S. satellite, launched in January 1958. It discovered the Van Allen radiation belts around Earth.

◆ Over 70 Explorers have now been launched to study the Sun, distant stars, and Earth itself.

◆ The only common link between all the Explorer satellites is that they use automated instruments to take scientific measurements.

◆ One of the most successful Explorers was the *Uhuru* satellite, which mapped the sky in X rays for the first time and also found the first signs of a black hole in space.

satellites are not all the same because they are designed to do different jobs. Many of the satellites fall into groups studying special fields of science. Interplanetary monitoring platforms (IMPs) studied the activity of the Sun. During the Apollo Moon missions they were used to watch for dangerous solar flares that could have injured astronauts on the Moon's surface.

These satellites were followed by the three International Sun-Earth Explorers (ISEEs). In 1985, seven years after launch, *ISEE-3* became the first space probe to explore a comet. NASA engineers put the satellite into a new orbit passing close to the Moon. Each time it passed the Moon, the pull of gravity speeded up the probe until it had enough speed to escape into interplanetary space and meet up with Comet Giacobini–Zinner. This gravitational slingshot was the same method used in 1977 to send the Voyager spaceprobes to the outer planets.

Other Explorers studied Earth rather than space. The Atmospheric Explorers looked into Earth's atmosphere to study its chemical make-up. The GEOS satellites were used to measure changes in Earth's gravity over different parts of its surface. Any changes to their predicted orbits revealed that the gravity pulling on them had gotten stronger or weaker. A map of these changes, called the geoid (JEE-oyd), can reveal the exact shape of Earth and help to show undersea features.

LOOK CLOSER

Uhuru

One of the most famous and successful Explorer satellites was *Uhuru*, the first X-ray astronomy satellite. Before its launch, astronomers had very little idea of which objects in space gave out X rays—they had to rely on detectors carried above the atmosphere for a few minutes on board rockets. During its nine-year life, *Uhuru* allowed scientists to map the sky in X rays for the first time. Its most important discovery was the rapidly changing X rays from a strong source near a faint star in the constellation Cygnus. Astronomers realized they were looking for the first time at the energy released by an invisible black hole in orbit around the faint star.

Astronomy explorers

Another successful group of Explorers, the International Ultraviolet Explorer (IUE) and the Extreme Ultraviolet Explorer (EUVE), were dedicated to astronomy. Because Earth's atmosphere absorbs so much of the radiation coming from space, satellites are an ideal way of discovering information that is hidden from ground-based astronomers. Ultraviolet light, for example, is emitted by very hot stars and gas in space. X rays and gamma rays are even more powerful and are emitted by the most violent objects in the Universe: supernovas (exploding stars) and black holes.

The Cosmic Background Explorer (COBE) was a telescope designed to make a map of the weakest radiation in the Universe. This is the background radiation left behind after the big bang that created everything. Today, this afterglow has cooled to –457°F (–270°C). However, COBE successfully detected the heat from it and found tiny variations between different areas of the sky. This showed that, in the instant it was created, the Universe was already forming the clumps of matter that became today's galaxies, stars, and planets.

CHECK THESE OUT!
✔NASA ✔SATELLITE ✔SPACE SCIENCE

Explosives

Chemicals that can release large amounts of energy very quickly

The most destructive substances ever invented are explosives. A single nuclear explosion in 1945 destroyed almost the entire Japanese city of Hiroshima. Explosions caused by trapped natural gas can demolish whole streets, and terrorist explosions have blown airplanes from the sky and skyscrapers into rubble. However, low-power explosives are used for fireworks displays on July 4 and to send flares high into the sky from ships in distress. One high explosive, nitroglycerin, can be used in a diluted state to treat people with heart disease.

How explosives work

Most explosives involve a source of carbon and a source of oxygen that combine together to form a large volume of carbon dioxide gas at high pressure. Carbon and oxygen may be in the same chemical compound, as in nitroglycerine, or in different compounds in a mixture, as in gunpowder. Before the explosion, the oxygen is usually combined with nitrogen, so the explosion releases nitrogen as well as carbon dioxide. Enormous amounts of energy are produced when the explosion occurs. This energy produces the massive shock wave of an explosion that can knock down walls and blow out windows.

The greater the amount of energy produced, the higher the pressure of the gas, and the higher the power of the explosion.

For explosives to be both safe and useful, they must be designed to explode in a controlled way. The process of setting off an explosion is called detonation. Explosives can be detonated electrically (when rocks are blasted in a quarry using a very long length of cable and a push-down plunger), by a physical shock (when a shell is fired from a rifle by pulling a trigger), or by heating them (when fireworks are set alight).

Types of explosives

Explosives are classified in many different ways, but there are really only three main types: primary explosives, low explosives, and high explosives. Primary explosives (one example is called lead azide) are very sensitive to heat and are used mainly to detonate other types of explosives called low explosives and high explosives.

Low explosives explode relatively slowly and burn rather than detonate. The low explosive gunpowder is the first known explosive. It was invented by the Chinese and has been used since the 13th century to fire bullets and shells. Fireworks and flares are also made of low explosives.

High explosives are much more spectacular and destructive than low explosives. A common high explosive called nitroglycerin explodes at a rate 25 times

Instruments around this gunpowder fireball are used to measure the heat given off.

HIGHLIGHTS

- When explosives are detonated (set off), they produce large amounts of gas that expand at a very high speed.

- Many explosives produce carbon dioxide and nitrogen gases.

- There are three main types of explosives: primary, low, and high explosives.

- Although explosives can be destructive, they can also be very useful. They are used in mining and quarrying and in automobile airbags.

greater than gunpowder. The gas produced in this way takes up around 3,000 times as much space as the original liquid explosive. Other high explosives include trinitrotoluene (TNT), cyclonite (RDX), and pentaerythritol tetranitrate (PETN), which is used to make a powerful explosive material called Semtex. The most powerful high explosives explode at up to 18,000 miles per hour (29,000 km/h) and generate temperatures as high as 9032°F (5000°C).

Uses of explosives

Explosives are best known as the destructive power behind bullets, grenades, and other weapons of war. Explosives also have other uses. Mining and quarrying rely on the use of high explosives such as dynamite, which is nitroglycerin absorbed into long sticks of clay to make it safer to use. The airbags used in

DISCOVERERS

E. I. Du Pont de Nemours

One of the world's biggest chemical companies, E. I. Du Pont de Nemours (called Du Pont), started out as an explosives manufacturer. When Frenchman Eleuthère Irénée Du Pont (1771–1834) moved to the United States in 1800, he found that U.S. gunpowder was more expensive and less effective than the explosives he had used in France. He set up a factory to make explosives using potassium nitrate (saltpeter) imported from India. Later, the Du Pont company found a better way of making explosives from another chemical called sodium nitrate, which was available in the much nearer country of Chile. The new method produced better explosives that were also less expensive.

automobiles are a less familiar use of explosives. They inflate (blow up) when the impact of a car crash detonates a small pellet of sodium azide explosive. A large amount of nitrogen gas is produced, which flows into the airbag to help protect the driver and passenger during a crash.

Another unexpected use of one particular explosive compound is in treating a type of heart disease called angina (an-JY-nuh). This disease commonly occurs when deposits of fat build up in the arteries (blood vessels leading away from the heart) and so make it harder for blood to flow through a person's body. Patients suffering from this disease will feel pain after exercise, when the heart needs to pump more blood. They are often given nitroglycerin tablets, which cause the blood vessels to expand, allowing blood to flow more freely and relieving the pain.

There are many other uses for explosives. High explosives are sometimes used to clear land when earthmoving equipment would take too long. Less powerful explosives are used to join metal fasteners called blind rivets that are often used in aircraft. Explosives are also used to produce diamonds for industrial use.

CHECK THESE OUT!
✔CARBON ✔CHEMICAL REACTION ✔OXYGEN

Extinction

The death of a species of living organism

The fossil record shows that the history of life on Earth has been repeatedly interrupted by a number of extinction events. Extinctions occur when unusually large numbers of organisms die out, and disappear from the record, at the same time. Most species (types) of living organisms survive for only a few million years and then die out or evolve into one or more new species. There is also a continuous background extinction and evolution going on. It is estimated that more than 99 percent of all the species that ever existed in the past are now extinct.

An extinction may happen in an isolated region or it may affect the whole of Earth. It may have different causes, ranging from volcanic eruptions to impacts of large extraterrestrial bodies such as asteroids, or to human destructiveness. There have been at least five major worldwide extinction events over the last 500 million years and many more smaller extinctions. At present, humans are altering the global environment to such an extent that many species are being wiped out each year.

Archaeopteryx was the first bird. It lived in the late Jurassic period.

HIGHLIGHTS

◆ Scientists estimate that at least 99 percent of all species that ever existed are now extinct.

◆ Over the last 500 million years, there have been at least five major extinction events in the world.

◆ The best known extinction event killed off the dinosaurs and many other organisms at the end of the Cretaceous period, over 66.4 million years ago.

◆ Over the last few thousand years, climate change and humans have wiped out most of the larger mammals on Earth.

Causes of mass extinction

Earth's geological (rock) record shows that its history has been one of changes. These changes have been driven mostly by internal Earth processes such as movements of crustal plates (the outer layer of Earth), periods of mountain building, volcanic activity, ice ages, sea level changes, and rapid climate changes. However, extraterrestrial events also played their part, such as the collision of extraterrestrial bodies with Earth. Over 30 large asteroids or comets have hit Earth in the last 500 million years. Any one of these processes and events could in themselves cause an extinction event. In combination, they are even more likely to disturb life on such a scale as to cause an extinction with abnormally high numbers of organisms dying out.

The first major extinction occurred around 438 million years ago at the end of the Ordovician (AWR-duh-VIH-shun) period, when over 50 percent of all species were wiped out. The combination of an ice age and a rapid drop in sea level are thought to have been responsible.

The most disastrous extinction of all was at the end of the Permian period (245 million years ago), when about 95 percent of all organisms were killed off. Most of these were sea creatures, such as trilobites (TRY-luh-BYTS), whose habitats were destroyed by a huge drop in sea level. This was caused by the joining together of several continental plates to form a supercontinent called Pangaea. There were many volcanic eruptions, which produced rapid climate change. This had a serious effect on land-living creatures.

The most famous extinction event occurred at the end of the Cretaceous (krih-TAY-shuhs) period, when dinosaurs and ammonites died out. The extinction coincided with an extraterrestrial impact and widespread volcanic activity. Experts are still trying to work out exactly why some creatures became extinct while others survived, and what the exact cause was.

Extinction today

Since the end of the last ice age, many mammals have become extinct. During the last ice age, giant deer, mammoths, and woolly rhinoceroses roamed Asia and Europe. In the Americas, nearly half the large mammals, including the mammoths, ground sloths, giant beavers, and saber-toothed cats, have become extinct. Some 33 groups of species have become extinct. Other mammals such as tigers and panda bears are now likely to become extinct. These losses coincide with humans' advanced hunting methods. Again, there has been a combination of causes of extinction—climate change and human activities.

CHECK THESE OUT!
✔CLIMATE ✔CRETACEOUS PERIOD
✔FOSSIL ✔GEOLOGIC TIMESCALE ✔ICE AGE
✔PERMIAN PERIOD ✔PLATE TECTONICS

LOOK CLOSER

Chicxulub

At the end of the Cretaceous period, around 66.4 million years ago, a massive object around 6 miles (10 km) wide hit Earth with devastating effects. Probably a meteorite, it blasted a hole 60 miles (100 km) wide and 7 miles (12 km) deep, near what is now the village of Chicxulub on the coast of Mexico's Yucatán peninsula. The crater walls fell inward, leaving collapse rings up to 90 miles (150 km) away from the point of impact. Around 12,000 cubic miles (50,000 cubic km) of limestone rock were blasted into the atmosphere. They were reduced to dust and droplets of molten rock by the impact.

The impact would have generated devastating earthquakes, giant waves called tsunamis (soo-NAH-meez), global outbreaks of wildfire, and acid rain. The dust blotted out the Sun, perhaps for months, causing global cooling. It is likely that, on a regional scale in the Americas, life would have been devastated. Globally, vulnerable groups of animals and plants would have suffered and some may have been pushed to extinction.

Scientists know that around this time there were vast outpourings of lavas in the Deccan region of western India. Such largescale volcanic events throw huge volumes of greenhouse gases such as carbon dioxide into the atmosphere. These gases can cause rapid global warming, the gradual rise in the temperature of Earth. Consequently, the extinction, when the dinosaurs and the ammonites died out, may well have been caused by a combination of events.

The Chicxulub impact crater was formed by the meteorite that may have caused the extinction of the dinosaurs 66.4 million years ago.

Fault

A break in Earth's rocks across which there is some relative movement

Many rocks do not stretch or bend easily. Some are brittle and may respond to the forces within Earth by breaking. Fault fractures (breaks) are common features within the rocks of Earth's crust. Active faulting is concentrated in great lines around Earth (the plate boundaries). There are faults miles away from these regions. These fractures in the rock occur on all scales from less than an inch to hundreds of miles.

Large faults such as those belonging to the San Andreas fault system of California can be seen from space as lines cutting through hills and valleys. The planes of fracture (the line of the break) also can extend deep underground many miles into Earth. When a fault happens, there is a sudden release of energy that sends shockwaves throughout the rocks of the surrounding region. These waves are felt as earthquakes.

Active faults

The most active fault zones are linked to regions that suffer the most earthquakes. Earthquakes and faults occur along the length of mountain ranges on land and along the mid-ocean ridges under the sea. These major features of Earth's surface are where Earth's internal forces break through to the surface at plate boundaries.

HIGHLIGHTS

◆ Many rocks are brittle and in response to forces within Earth they break along fault planes.

◆ It is the energy that is released by faulting that produces earthquakes.

◆ Large faults such as those of California's San Andreas system can be seen from space.

The faults of the midocean ridge are all fairly shallow and close to the surface. They result from the ocean floor rocks being pulled apart as heat rises from within Earth and partially melts the rocks to form basalt lavas (LAH-vuhz) and new ocean floor rocks. Stretching causes the rocks to break and form down-stepping rift valley faults and sideways-growing transform faults. Stretching of continental crust rocks produces similar rift valleys such as the 6,000-mile- (9,660-km-) long Great Rift Valley of east Africa.

In this thrust fault, older rock is being pushed over younger rock, and the fault line is clearly visible.

Where ocean floor rocks are pushed aside and slide down below the edge of the continents, the seabed is dragged down for several miles to form deep sea trenches. These trenches mark great fault zones called subduction zones that dip down for hundreds of miles below the edge of the continents. As ocean floor rocks move down subduction zones, the grinding friction sets off earthquakes and partially melts rocks to form volcanoes. Other faults splay off subduction zones and break through to the surface. This combination of submarine trenches, subduction zones, earthquakes, volcanoes, and associated faults is particularly found around the so-called Pacific Ring of Fire, which stretches clockwise from New Zealand through Japan, Alaska, Washington State on the Pacific coast of the United States, and Chile in South America.

Plate movements on land also generate great fault movements, especially those associated with building young mountain ranges such as the Himalayas. As the Indian continental plate continues to push northward into southern Asia, rocks have been compressed, thrown into great folds, and broken along many fault lines. Over millions of years, these faults and folds can dislocate rocks by tens of hundreds of miles.

Many different types of faults can be formed, depending on the forces that make them and the angles at which the rocks lie. The most common faults, called normal faults, have a vertical or nearly vertical fault plane, and the rocks on one side slip down. Horizontal forces produce almost flat-lying fault planes called low-angle thrust faults, over which whole mountains can be pushed for many miles. Other horizontal forces can produce vertical fault planes, called tear or strike-slip faults, along which there are horizontal sideways movements, and the ground just seems to tear open.

Ancient fault zones can be economically important if they contain valuable mineral ores. The development of faults deep underground provides the conditions under which mineral-rich solutions can move through the rocks. Minerals can grow within and around the crushed rocks of the fault zone. Silvermines at Navan in Ireland— the largest lead–silver and zinc mine in Europe— is developed along an ancient deep fault.

LOOK CLOSER

San Andreas

The swarm of parallel faults that cut through the rocks and landscapes of the American Pacific coast for more than 800 miles (1,300 km) is named the San Andreas Fault. The San Andreas also cuts through San Francisco and is responsible for that city's many devastating earthquakes. In 1906, one of the faults moved up to 20 feet (6 m) at one time. The earth movements and fire destroyed a large part of the city and killed 700 people. The complex of faults result from the Pacific plate moving northwest and sliding beside and rubbing against the North American plate. The plates have moved about 10 miles (16 km) relative to one another over the last two million years.

CHECK THESE OUT!

✔EARTHQUAKE ✔GEOLOGY
✔LANDFORM ✔MOUNTAIN ✔OCEAN
✔PLATE TECTONICS ✔ROCK ✔VOLCANO

Fiber Optics

Sending light via thin strands over long distances without it fading or distorting

Light can be transmitted from one place to another over distances from just a few inches to hundreds of miles using the technique of fiber optics. Fiber optics uses glass or plastic optical fibers to transmit light without losing its intensity. Optical fibers can be used to carry information within a computer or halfway around the world.

Theory of fiber optics

Fiber optic technology relies on a type of reflection called total internal reflection, which can only happen when light is passing through a medium surrounded by a medium of different optical properties. Every transparent substance is described by a number, called its index of refraction, which tells how much a light beam will be bent when it enters the medium from the air. When light traveling through one medium strikes a boundary with a medium of higher index of refraction, some of the light is reflected and some escapes into the new medium. When the

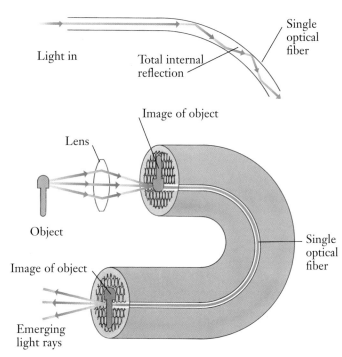

The image of the object is carried by the optical fibers. Cladding around each fiber prevents light escaping into the other fibers.

new medium has a lower index of refraction, and the angle at which light strikes the new medium is shallow enough, all of the light is reflected. When light is sent at a shallow angle into a glass fiber surrounded by air, it will simply bounce from one side to the other without any loss of brightness. This is total internal reflection.

Fiber optics uses total internal reflection to bounce light from side to side along a narrow tube. The reflection happens in just the same way as it does between air and water, but optical fibers use plastic and glass to contain and refract the light.

Making optical fibers

A single, tubelike optical fiber has a central core that carries the light and an outer coat, the cladding, that produces the total internal reflection and protects the core from damage. The narrowest optical fibers are one-tenth of the thickness of a human hair. Fiber cores are usually made of very pure, transparent (see-through)

THE FUTURE

Computing at the Speed of Light

Fiber optics could one day be used to transmit information inside computers. At present, the electronic components (parts) on silicon chips keep getting smaller and computers keep getting faster. Eventually, this miniaturization will reach its limit because electronics will not work below a certain scale. Optical computers, however, which would process, store, and transmit information using pulses of light, would have no size limitation, and could be 10,000 times faster than electronic computers. Scientists are now working on ways of copying a computer's separate components using light. Many problems, such as information storage, still have to be solved, however.

glass surrounded by plastic cladding. To make fibers, a rod of glass is heated in a furnace and long, thin strands are pulled from it.

Fibers thicker than 0.05 mm are called multimode fibers. They are the simplest to make and simple to use because it is quite easy to aim light into their open ends. One problem with multimode fibers is that the light rays can bounce around more inside them, interfering with each other and distorting a signal.

Thinner monomode fibers can overcome this problem. Monomode fibers are so thin it is difficult to get light into them. However, once inside, the light rays can travel only in a straight (or very nearly straight) line, reducing the number of reflections and allowing signals to travel over very long distances.

Fiber optics in action

Different types of fibers are used for different applications. One of the most important areas where optical fibers are used today is in communications, where they transmit signals in flashes of light. Optical fibers have many advantages over traditional electrical cables,

the most important being that they can carry signals with much less distortion.

Optical fibers usually carry information that is transmitted as on-off pulses of light. To send information at high speed over long distances (often thousands of miles through undersea cables), the light source at the transmitting end has to be bright and easily controllable. Over very long distances, however, even these bright signals can fade and become distorted, so repeater boxes are placed along cables at least every 30 miles (48 km). Repeaters receive the signals coming through one bundle of cables and resend them through the next.

Medicine and engineering use optical fibers in a different way. A fiberscope is a narrow tube containing thousands of optical fibers. It can be inserted into the human body or into machinery, and it transmits pictures to the other end of the fibers, where a camera transfers them to a television screen. Fiberscopes can have lights or tools attached to them so that their operators can carry out complicated tasks. This ability has led to keyhole surgery: tools are inserted through tiny slits in a person's skin, so the pain and recovery time from an operation are reduced.

CHECK THESE OUT!
✔ELECTRONICS ✔LASER ✔LIGHT ✔OPTICS

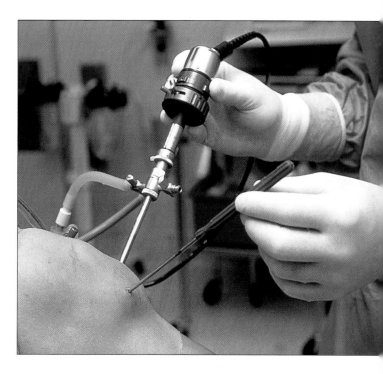

The fiberscope in the surgeon's left hand contains optical fibers that show any damage in the patient's knee. It is inserted through a tiny slit in the skin.

Fission

Nuclear explosions, nuclear submarines, and much of the electricity on which everyday living depends have one thing in common: power generated by nuclear fission (FIH-shuhn). Fission is the process that occurs when large atoms are split into smaller ones, usually releasing massive amounts of energy.

Physics of fission

Atoms are the building blocks of chemical elements such as carbon or oxygen. Atoms consist of smaller particles called protons, neutrons, and electrons. The protons and neutrons together make the central part of the atom called the nucleus (NOO-klee-uhs), while the electrons revolve around it. In theory it is possible to break large atoms into smaller particles in a process called fission.

Most atoms are stable (unchanging), but the largest atoms are generally unstable and can split (undergo fission) if neutrons are fired at them. The chemical element uranium (yoo-RAY-nee-uhm) is a good example. If a neutron is fired at a stable type of uranium called uranium 235, the uranium absorbs the neutron and becomes another type of uranium called uranium 236. This is so unstable that it splits into two smaller atoms, with the release of two or three neutrons. The extra neutrons can trigger other reactions. This process is called a chain reaction.

HIGHLIGHTS

◆ Fission is used in nuclear power plants, nuclear weapons, and nuclear submarines.

◆ During fission, a large atom is split into smaller ones, releasing energy and one or more neutrons.

◆ The released neutrons can trigger additional fission reactions resulting in a chain reaction. Uncontrolled, a chain reaction will lead to a meltdown or explosion.

Splitting large atoms into smaller atoms to produce energy

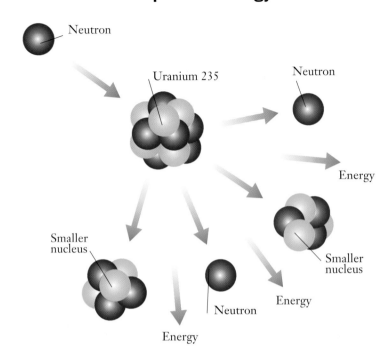

Fission starts when a lone neutron collides with the nucleus of a uranium 235 atom. This splits into two smaller nuclei and more lone neutrons.

The mass (the amount of material in an object) of a large atom such as uranium is actually slightly larger than the mass of the fragment atoms and neutrons into which it splits. The mass that seems to disappear when fission occurs is the energy produced by nuclear reactions. This energy is used in nuclear power plants and nuclear bombs.

History of fission

In 1896, French physicist Henri Becquerel (1852–1908) discovered that some atoms give off smaller particles in a process called radioactivity. Then British physicist Ernest Rutherford (1871–1937) successfully caused an atomic change. He produced atoms of oxygen by firing helium nuclei at nitrogen atoms. He showed the nucleus was made of building blocks that could be put together or taken apart.

The first fission reaction was demonstrated in 1938 by German chemists Otto Hahn (1879–1968) and Fritz Strassmann (1902–1980), who successfully split uranium. Their finding was explained the following year when Austrian physicist Lise Meitner (1878–1968) realized that the uranium nucleus had split into two much smaller atoms.

Nuclear power and nuclear weapons

During the early 1940s, Italian physicist Enrico Fermi (1901–1954) perfected the first useful nuclear reactor (also called a nuclear pile) at the University of Chicago. Although Fermi used uranium, other scientists found another method of generating (producing) energy from fission by creating a chemical element called plutonium (ploo-TOH-nee-uhm). In August 1945, massive nuclear bombs were dropped onto the Japanese cities of Hiroshima and Nagasaki. The bombs were equivalent to 15,000 tons (15,240 tonnes) and 21,000 tons (21,336 tonnes) of TNT. Together they killed or injured around 199,000 people, and left behind huge amounts of radioactivity that caused diseases for many years.

After World War II, nuclear fission was put to other uses. The U.S. Navy launched its first nuclear-powered submarine, *Nautilus*, in 1954. The first nuclear power plant was opened at Calder Hall in England in 1956. The United States saw its first plant open in Pennsylvania the following year. Similar plants opened around the world throughout the 1960s and 1970s, but not without problems.

The horrifying damage done by the nuclear bomb dropped on Hiroshima on August 6, 1945.

STORY OF SCIENCE

Einstein and the Bomb

In 1905, Albert Einstein (1879–1955), one of the world's greatest physicists, worked out that mass and energy are the same thing. He calculated that a tiny amount of mass (m) can produce a massive amount of energy (E) using his famous equation $E=mc^2$, where c is the speed of light. In 1939, just as World War II was breaking out, Einstein wrote to President Roosevelt to explain how nuclear fission could be used to produce massive amounts of energy. This prompted Roosevelt to authorize the Manhattan Project, in which some of the world's greatest physicists worked to produce the bombs that were dropped on Hiroshima and Nagasaki in 1945.

Nuclear power had been promised as a virtually free source of energy, but turned out to be much more expensive than other fuels such as coal. There are also concerns about how to dispose of radioactive waste and prevent the spread of nuclear weapons. The biggest setbacks for the nuclear industry were the nuclear accidents at Three Mile Island in Harrisburg, Pennsylvania, in 1979, and in Chernobyl, Ukraine, in 1996. Many people question whether the benefits of nuclear power are worth the risks.

CHECK THESE OUT!
✔ATOM ✔ENERGY ✔FUSION ✔NUCLEAR PHYSICS

Flood

An overflow of water, from rivers or the ocean, caused by a variety of conditions

The biblical story of Noah and the ark is believed to have been based on a huge flood that took place when the Euphrates (yoo-FRAY-teez) River in present-day Iraq overflowed its banks around 3000 B.C.E. Today, never a year goes by without many flooding disasters being reported from some part of the world.

Some floods are welcomed. The annual flooding of the Nile River in Egypt, for example, once helped to carry rich silt (sedimentary material in the water) to the plains of the Nile Valley, and made it one of the world's most fertile crop-producing regions. However, floods are more likely to bring death and destruction. In the United States alone, about 200 people lose their lives each year as a result of floods.

Types of floods

There are three basic types of floods. Rivers can overflow (generally after heavy rain), artificial structures such as dikes or dams can give way, or high seas can cause coastal flooding.

Sudden or continuous heavy rainfall is the most common cause of river floods. The rain saturates the land on both sides of the river, and

This flood in Argentina followed days of heavy rain, which overpowered the drainage system.

soon no more can drain into the river channel. The water rises and covers the land, creating a floodplain. This is what happened from April through July of 1993, when torrential rain fell almost continually in the Midwest. The flood left dozens of people dead and caused more than $10 billion worth of property damage.

When there is sudden heavy rainfall in mountain or desert regions, flash floods (very sudden floods) can be extremely dangerous for people caught unawares near a stream or river. Flash flooding is also caused by snowmelts or the sudden breaking of an ice jam (ice that holds back water). The floodplains along the Ohio and Mississippi Rivers and their tributaries (TRIH-byuh-ter-eez; the waterways that feed into them) have been the scene of extensive flood damage. In 1999, two river floods following closely on one another resulted in a disaster in Vietnam.

When a concrete or earthen dam (a barrier such as a Mississippi levee) fails, it can suddenly release millions of gallons of water. People who live downstream from a dam have suffered

HIGHLIGHTS

◆ The main types of floods are: river floods that are caused by heavy rain, floods caused by the failure of artificial structures such as dams and dikes, and coastal floods from high seas.

◆ Floods are usually very destructive. They can destroy crops and property, wash away fertile soil, and result in the deaths of many people.

◆ The 1993 floods in the Midwest caused more than $10 billion worth of damage.

False-color images can help scientists evaluate flood damage on a global scale. The red sections here show flooded forest.

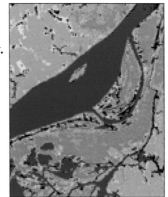

catastrophic damage in such situations. The most tragic dam collapse in the United States occurred in 1889 at Johnstown, Pennsylvania, killing more than 2,200 people.

Coastal floods can be due to one or more causes. After a hurricane, the wind can raise huge waves onshore. In the Southern Hemisphere, these storms are called typhoons (ty-FOONZ) or cyclones (SY-klohnz). Even an abnormally high tide can flow over or break through coastal defenses. A volcanic eruption or an earthquake, either from the ocean floor or on land close to the coast, can produce a giant tidal wave called a tsunami (soo-NAH-mee).

Controlling flood damage

Floods can cause the destruction of valuable farm animals, crops, or farmland, eroding millions of dollars worth of fertile soil. In the 20th century, many projects were started to control the periodic flooding of the bigger rivers in the United States. After the destructive flooding of the Mississippi in 1927, for example, Congress passed laws for a major plan of development. This plan allowed for the construction of a system of levees, floodways, dams, reservoirs, and channel improvements in an attempt to control the river and its tributaries during regular spring floods.

CHECK THESE OUT!
✔COAST ✔DELTA ✔EROSION
✔HURRICANE ✔MONSOON ✔RIVER

LOOK CLOSER

Some Major Floods of Recent Years

Floods have been caused all over the world by a number of different factors. Both the United States and Bangladesh in particular have been badly hit in recent years.

1938	China	To slow the advance of the Japanese army, the dikes controlling the flow of the Huang Ho (Yellow River) were destroyed by retreating Chinese troops: 90,000 human lives lost.
1943	United States	The Mississippi and its tributaries flooded 12 million acres (5 million ha), leaving 50,000 people homeless.
1946	Japan	A tsunami struck the islands of Honshu and Shikoku, leaving more than 100,000 people homeless and 1,800 dead.
1963	Northern Italy	The Vaiont Dam overflowed when a landslide fell into its reservoir, drowning more than 2,000 people in villages below the dam.
1970	Bangladesh	A cyclone on the Ganges delta resulted in more than 300,000 people dead.
1972	United States	Hurricane Agnes caused rivers to flood in New York and Pennsylvania, causing over $3 billion damage and leaving more than 15,000 people homeless.
1976	Philippines	A tsunami approaching from the Celebes Sea reached 98 feet (30 m) in height and caused 5,000 deaths.
1985	Bangladesh	A cyclone produced flooding resulting in 11,000 deaths.
1988	Sudan	Flooding of the Nile left more than 800 people dead and 28 million homeless.
1991	Bangladesh	Waves due to a cyclone flooded plains, killing 200,000 and leaving millions homeless.
1993	United States	The Mississippi and Missouri, and their tributaries, flooded more than 10 million acres (4 million ha) of land in Illinois, Iowa, Kansas, Kentucky, Minnesota, Missouri, Nebraska, North Dakota, South Dakota, and Wisconsin; 50 people died; 70,000 were left homeless.
1999	Venezuela	Torrential rains produced mud slides, which buried between 30,000 and 50,000 people.

Force

Any influence that causes objects to change their speed or direction of motion

Influences that hold things together, drive them apart, and change their motion are called forces. Forces act on all objects, from the tiniest subatomic particles to the largest stars in the Universe. Greek and Roman thinkers believed that an object would keep moving only if a force were constantly applied to it. This view came from everyday experience. A cart will slow down and stop if it is not pulled, for example.

Italian scientist Galileo Galilei (1564–1642) had different ideas. When studying the motions of objects, he noticed that a ball gains speed as it rolls into a dip. When it rolls up the other side of the dip, it slows down until it comes to rest and then starts to roll back. Noting that the ball did not quite reach the height of the original starting point, Galileo decided that friction (FRIK-shuhn; a rubbing force) was draining some of the ball's energy. Take away the friction, he reasoned, and the ball would rise to the same height on the opposite side of the dip. If the far side of the dip were less steep, the ball would travel farther before it reached the same height. If the far side were completely flat, the ball would keep rolling forever without reaching the original height. British scientist Sir Isaac Newton (1642–1727) developed this idea into his first law of motion.

In a vacuum, objects of different masses fall at the same speed. Air resistance prevents this on Earth.

HIGHLIGHTS

◆ There are four different basic forces. These are gravitational, electromagnetic, strong nuclear, and weak nuclear forces.

◆ The forces between electrically charged objects are related to the forces between magnets. Both are forms of electromagnetic force.

◆ A force called electromagnetic repulsion is responsible for preventing solid objects from passing through each other.

◆ Nuclear forces have no effect outside the nucleus.

Gravity

Although gravity (GRA-vuh-tee) was the first force to be observed, it has always been poorly understood. Early thinkers were baffled because they believed that a pull or push was necessary for an object to move, yet the pull of gravity worked on falling objects without any other objects touching them until they landed.

Newton studied the planets in motion to gain an understanding of gravity. By Newton's first law, planets would move in straight lines if no forces were acting on them. Planets move in circular orbits around the Sun, however, and they have moons that orbit them in similar paths. For an object to move in a circle, there must always be a force pulling it toward the center of the circle. Just as a slingshot pulls a rock when it is swung around, so a planet is pulled toward the center of its orbit by gravity. The same pulling force makes unsupported objects fall to the ground on Earth.

In 1687, Newton put forward his law of gravity. He proposed that the gravitational force between two objects was related to their masses and to the distance between them. The mathematical expression of this law is

$$F = \frac{GM_1M_2}{r^2}$$

where M_1 and M_2 are the objects' masses and r is the distance between them. G is a number called the universal constant of gravitation.

Newton had no idea what caused the gravitational attraction between objects. For more than two centuries, scientists used Newton's law of gravity without understanding the cause of gravity. In 1915, German-born U.S. physicist Albert Einstein (1879–1955) put forward his general theory of relativity. He suggested that gravity was caused by the masses of objects distorting the three dimensions of

Parachutist is drawn to Earth

Direction of force

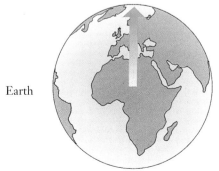

Earth

A parachutist falls toward the ground on Earth. Earth's gravity pulls objects toward itself and even holds the Moon in orbit.

DISCOVERERS

Galileo Galilei

Mathematician, astronomer, and physicist Galileo Galilei was born near Pisa, Italy, in 1564. At the time of Galileo's birth, scientists were still following the theories of early Greek philosopher Aristotle (384–322 B.C.E.). Aristotle had suggested that Earth was the center of a spherical Universe made of five elements—earth, water, air, fire, and a fifth element called aither. In Aristotle's theory, each element had a different density (heaviness) so that objects would rise or fall according to the elements of which they were made. Fire would rise and earth would fall, for example. Aristotle had also incorrectly stated that a heavier object must fall to Earth much faster than a lighter object.

By the time of Galileo, Aristotle's theories had been popular for so long that few had thought to challenge them. Galileo was an exception. In 1589, he proved part of Aristotle's theory wrong by dropping two objects from the top of Pisa's leaning tower. Although the objects had different weights, both reached the ground at the same time.

Galileo died in 1642 near Florence. More than 300 years later, in August 1971, Galileo's experiment was repeated on the Moon. *Apollo 15* commander David Scott dropped a feather and a hammer at the same time. Because the Moon has no atmosphere, the feather's drop was not slowed as it would be on Earth. The hammer and the feather landed at the same time.

space (height, depth, width) and the fourth dimension of time. The more recent theory of superstrings uses 10 dimensions to explain gravity and the other basic forces together.

Electromagnetic forces

The forces of attraction and repulsion between electrically charged objects and between magnetic objects have been known since ancient times. The ancient Greeks knew that rubbing a

rod of amber with animal fur gave the rod the ability to attract bits of straw. Around the same time, the Chinese discovered the magnetic properties of magnetite, a form of iron oxide.

In the 18th century, French physicist Charles Coulomb (1736–1806) measured the forces between electrically charged objects. He realized that the equation for these forces had the same form as Newton's law of gravity. The mathematical expression of Coulomb's law is:

$$F = \frac{KQ_1Q_2}{r^2}$$

where Q_1 and Q_2 are charges on the objects, and r is the distance between the charged objects. The force F pulls the charged objects together if they have opposite charges and pushes them apart if they have like charges.

Danish physicist Hans Christian Ørsted (1777–1851) made the first connection between electrical and magnetic forces. In 1820, he noted that an electrical current flowing through a wire moved a compass needle. The current was producing a magnetic field. British physicist James Clark Maxwell (1831–1879) calculated the mathematical relationships between electrical and magnetic forces. He found they were both forms of a single force called the electromagnetic force.

Electromagnetic forces are transmitted by the exchange of particles that have no mass, called photons, between objects. Contact forces between objects rely on electromagnetic forces. When two objects are in contact, the electrons in their surface atoms interact. Repulsions between the like charges of surface electrons prevent solid objects from passing through one another.

Forces in the nucleus

The nucleus (NOO-klee-uhs; center) of an atom contains all the positive charge of the atom bundled together in a tiny space. Normally, the electromagnetic repulsion between the positively charged protons would drive them apart. Atomic nuclei are stable, however, so there must be a powerful force that holds together protons and neutrons (uncharged particles). This force is called the strong nuclear force, or simply the strong force. The strong force involves the exchange of unstable particles called mesons.

THE FUTURE

GUTs, TOEs, and Superstrings

Scientists use models to help understand how matter and energy behave. Aristotle's theory of elements was an early model for understanding the properties of substances. The current search is for a model, called a unified field theory, that can explain the origins of all the forces that hold matter together and control its behavior. These are called grand unification theories (GUTs) or theories of everything (TOEs).

One theory describes superstrings as the basic form of matter. These massless strings are absolutely tiny (10^{-36} m long). They vibrate in 10 dimensions of space and time, and different vibrations correspond to different particles. Four of the space-time dimensions are familiar: height, depth, width, and time. The remaining six dimensions are said to be compactified, or invisible.

Compactified dimensions can be explained by thinking about the appearance of a sphere. From any single point of view, and with lighting that does not cast shadows, a sphere appears to be a two-dimensional circle. Lighting the sphere from the side reveals the third dimension. A shadow appears that shows the sphere's depth. In a similar way, the compactified dimensions become noticeable when other properties are observed.

Superstring theory can explain all types of forces as interactions between superstrings. The problem is that it cannot yet explain how particles have mass. Also, the calculations that show how gravity works require a new type of matter—called shadow matter—to exist. Many more calculations and experiments will have to be completed before the superstring theory can be confirmed.

LOOK CLOSER

Newton's Laws

British scientist Sir Isaac Newton was born in 1642, the same year that Galileo died. He worked on Galileo's ideas about forces and put them in a practical form. The resulting statements came to be called Newton's laws. Newton died in 1727.

Newton's first law: a body will continue in uniform motion unless a force acts on it. In other words, an object moving at a steady speed in a fixed direction will continue to do so unless a force changes its speed or direction of motion. A stationary object is also in uniform motion, but its speed is zero. It will start to move only if a force causes it to do so.

Newton's second law: force = mass x acceleration ($F = ma$)

If a force (F) causes an object of mass (m) to accelerate with acceleration (a), then twice the force will be needed to cause an object with mass 2m to accelerate at the same rate. If a force 2F acts on the first object, of mass m, then it will accelerate at twice the original rate.

Force and acceleration are examples of vector (VEK-tuhr) quantities: they have both size and direction. A force causes acceleration in the direction of the force. An object will slow down if a force acts on it in the opposite direction to its motion because the force is causing a backward acceleration, or deceleration.

Newton's third law: for every action there is an equal and opposite reaction.

This law is useful for calculating the forces for separate objects when they interact. In the diagram below, the force on the tennis ball is matched by an opposite force on the racket that hits it. A block on a stretched spring experiences a force toward the spring that is matched by an opposite force in the spring.

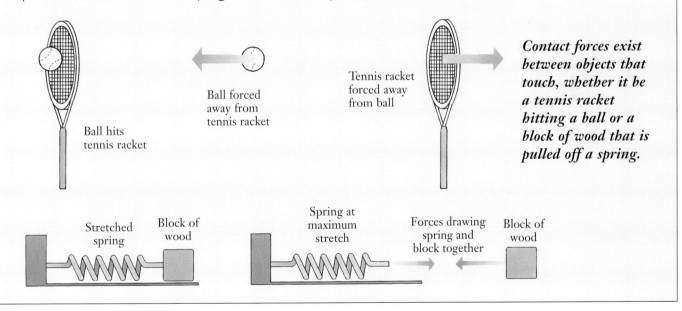

Ball hits tennis racket

Ball forced away from tennis racket

Tennis racket forced away from ball

Contact forces exist between objects that touch, whether it be a tennis racket hitting a ball or a block of wood that is pulled off a spring.

Stretched spring   Block of wood

Spring at maximum stretch

Forces drawing spring and block together

Block of wood

Most physicists believe protons, neutrons, and mesons are built of particles called quarks, which have a property similar to electric charge. At extremely close range, the strong force is around 100 times greater than electromagnetic forces. The strong force trails off so quickly that it is not felt outside the nucleus.

There is a second force that acts in the nucleus. It is called the weak nuclear force because it is many times weaker than the strong force or electromagnetic force. The weak nuclear force is stronger than the gravitational force, but it is only involved in a number of very slow processes, for example, the radioactive decay of unstable isotopes that emit beta particles (electrons) or positrons.

CHECK THESE OUT!
✔ELECTROMAGNETISM ✔GRAVITY
✔NEWTONIAN PHYSICS ✔NUCLEAR PHYSICS

Forest

Dense growth of trees covering a large area

A group of many trees growing closely together over a large area is called a forest. A forest is also a habitat, a place where particular plants, animals, and other organisms live. A forest has different soil and a different climate (an area's regular weather pattern) from surrounding areas that are bare of trees.

There are three basic types of forests: coniferous forests, deciduous (dih-SIH-juh-wuhs; also called broad-leaved) forests, and tropical forests. Climate is the most important influence on the type of forest that grows.

The three main types of forests are found mostly in different regions. Coniferous forests are found mainly in the cold regions of the Northern Hemisphere. Deciduous forests grow mainly in temperate regions between the tropics and the polar regions. Tropical forests grow

Forests and woodlands are grouped in areas around the world where they are best able to grow. Different trees require different conditions.

HIGHLIGHTS

◆ There are three basic types of forests: coniferous forests, deciduous forests, and tropical forests.

◆ Climate and altitude both influence the types of trees found in a forest.

mainly in the hot zones around the equator. Altitude also influences the trees that grow. Even near the equator, conifers and deciduous trees (those that shed their leaves every fall) similar to those in colder regions may grow on high mountain slopes that are much colder than low-lying areas nearby. The lie of the land may influence the types of trees found. For example, in mountainous areas, south-facing slopes bathed in sunlight for most of the day may support different types of trees from steep, west-facing slopes that receive only afternoon sunlight.

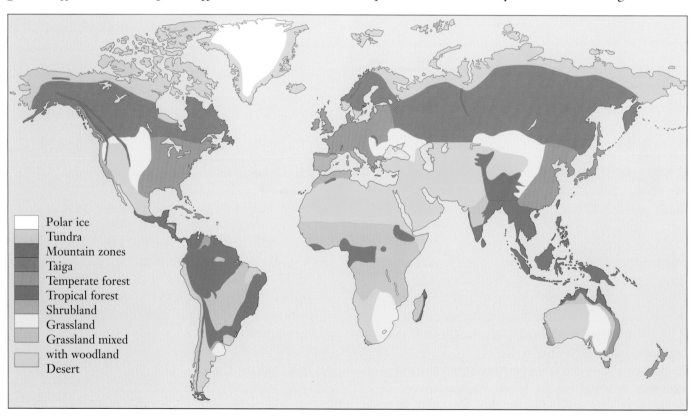

Polar ice
Tundra
Mountain zones
Taiga
Temperate forest
Tropical forest
Shrubland
Grassland
Grassland mixed
with woodland
Desert

LOOK CLOSER

Destruction of the Rain Forests

The destruction of the world's rain forests would mean the loss of millions of plant and animal species. It is likely that many unrecorded species are being lost now. Yet these unique forests are currently being cut down at an alarmingly fast rate and for a number of different reasons. Farmers and ranchers are burning the forests of the Amazon to clear land to raise crops and graze livestock. In Peru the forests are being cleared to grow crops including coca, which is used to make the drug cocaine. However, the forest soil is poor and infertile, so farmers and ranchers do not get high crop yields or rich grazing lands. Some of the newly cleared areas have now been abandoned, which has led to massive erosion (the wearing away of the soil) in areas that were once productive, untouched forest.

Logging companies also contribute to the destruction of the rain forests. They cut down huge numbers of trees to sell the timber. The logging industry is destroying rain forests in many parts of the world, particularly in Brazil and Southeast Asia. There, as elsewhere, rain forests are also cut down for fuel, to make way for mining developments, and to build new roads and towns.

The burning of the rain forests releases large amounts of the gas carbon dioxide into the atmosphere. Scientists have warned that the buildup of carbon dioxide in the air is one of the causes behind the general warming of Earth's atmosphere (global warming).

Cutting down trees turns rich forests into barren landscapes.

The amount of rainfall an area receives also influences the kinds of trees that grow there. Most species (types) of trees cannot survive in dry or semidesert regions. Those that can often have deep roots that reach far underground to find water. They have tiny leaves or leaves shaped like needles that lose very little moisture to the hot, dry air. Very different species thrive in rain forests where heavy rain falls almost every day.

Coniferous forests

Conifers grow mainly in the far north. These cone-bearing trees are mainly evergreen: they keep their leaves all year round. In harsh winter weather, conifers provide shelter for the animals of the forest.

The northern coniferous forest, called the taiga (TY-guh), forms a belt of dense woodland 500 miles (800 km) wide. The taiga circles the Northern Hemisphere, stretching right across Asia, North America, and northern Europe. This great forest belt separates the Arctic tundra (the barren, treeless lowlands of the far north) from the temperate woodlands to the south. Winters in the north are long and bitterly cold. Summers are short and mild, with long hours of daylight. The trees of taiga forests include fir and spruce.

Coniferous trees also grow in some forests further south. Pines, tamarack, and hemlock are plentiful in areas that receive high rainfall. Huge sequoias and giant redwoods, the largest living plants, are conifers that grow in California.

Deciduous forests

South of the taiga, in temperate regions, the climate is milder with cold winters, warm summers, and high rainfall. The forests of temperate regions include mainly deciduous or broad-leaved trees. Deciduous trees shed their leaves each fall to help them survive the cold winters. New leaves grow again each spring. Maple, oak, beech, hickory, and linden are common species in deciduous forests.

The leaves shed by deciduous trees enrich the soil beneath them. Various species of plants thrive alongside the trees where the tree canopy (cover) is lighter. Some plants bear fruits and berries in the fall, on which the forest animals feed and hoard for the winter. Grasses, mosses, and wild mushrooms may also cover the ground.

Like the coniferous and tropical forests, deciduous forests are important sources of timber for human use. The wood is used to make everything from houses to furniture and matchsticks. Deciduous forests cover about 6.5 million square miles (almost 17 million sq km). This is about 12 percent of Earth's land area. Parts of the Black Forest in Germany and much of the United States's New England woodlands contain deciduous trees.

Some parts of the world, such as parts of Australia, Asia, Africa, and South America, have long, dry winters and hot, humid summers. This climate encourages the growth of a type of forest called dry or monsoon forest. Broad-leaved trees here shed their leaves during the dry season and grow them again with the heavy monsoon rains.

Tropical forests

Many types of trees grow in tropical forests. They include mahogany, an evergreen, and tropical forms of deciduous trees such as teak. Common plants include vines (lianas) and epiphytes (EH-puh-fyts), which are also called air plants because they grow perched on tree branches with their roots in the air. Epiphytes include many kinds of orchids, which obtain their food and water from the air and from material caught in crannies in the trunks.

Tropical rain forests are woodlands that receive at least 100 inches (25 m) of rain each year. They mainly occupy low-lying areas around

LOOK CLOSER

Forest Water

The world's rain forests thrive in areas that receive huge amounts of water—between 80 and 200 inches (20 and 50 m) of rain each year. To some extent, these forests create their own climate, and they also influence the climate of surrounding regions. When it rains, the forest trees act like giant sponges, soaking up the moisture and preventing it from running off into streams and rivers. The trees draw up the water through their roots and later release it through their leaves as water vapor in a process called transpiration. In the air, the water droplets gather together to form clouds that bring more rain. In this way the moisture in rain forests is recycled.

When large areas of rain forest are cut down, this cycle is stopped. Destruction of the rain forests can lead to drought (excessive dryness) because the amount of moisture in the air has been reduced.

Rain forests also affect the climate of surrounding regions in other ways. They act as giant windbreaks and influence the air currents. Cutting down the forest may result in changes to wind patterns that can lead to drought, and the rain forest soil is very thin so it will easily wash away when not bound together by tree roots.

the equator and cover a total of 1.5 million square miles (3.9 million sq km). Almost 60 percent of the world's tropical rain forest is found in the Amazon region of South America. Other large rain forests lie in Indonesia, Zaire, Papua New Guinea, and Myanmar. Tropical rain forests are a vital habitat for living organisms. They cover only 6 percent of the world's land area, but they are home to more than 50 percent of all the plant and animal species on Earth.

Some parts of the tropics receive a much lower rainfall, less than 20 inches (50 cm) of rain each year. In these areas, thorn forests are common. They grow in parts of Africa, Australia, Mexico, and South America. The thorn-bearing trees tangle and interlace their branches, forming a forbidding barrier to animals and people. These forests also yield some products that are useful to people, including gums, fruits, and rubber.

Five layers of the forest

From the tips of the tallest trees to ground level, scientists recognize five layers of living things in forests. Each layer forms a habitat for different living organisms. The topmost layer has the tallest trees and is therefore called the emergent layer. Long vines wind around the trees. High in the air, epiphytes hang from trunks and branches. Younger and shorter trees form the next two layers, which grow closely together to form a leafy canopy that shades the lower layers. Lack of sunlight prevents these trees from reaching their full height. If one of the larger canopy trees falls, a smaller tree will grow taller and spread its leaves in the patch of sunlight.

The fourth layer, the understory, contains seedlings, bushes, ferns, and shrubs, which form the thickest layer of the rain forest. Unlike trees that have a single woody trunk, most shrubs and bushes have many stems and thick leaves. The fourth layer contains plants without woody stems, such as grasses, flowers, and ferns. The lushness of this layer depends on how much sunlight manages to penetrate the layers above.

The fifth layer is the forest floor, also called the ground cover. Almost all direct sunlight is caught by the mass of plants above, so the forest floor is dark and shady. Dead branches, leaves, and the remains of living organisms drop to the ground to enrich the soil. Thousands of small and microscopic creatures that live on the forest floor, including worms, insects, fungi, and bacteria, act like living garbage disposal units. They consume the plant and animal remains and help to return the goodness they contain to the soil. What was once a living organism becomes a natural fertilizer to feed tomorrow's plants.

CHECK THESE OUT!
✔CLIMATE ✔EROSION ✔GLOBAL WARMING

A tropical forest gets much darker from treetops to ground level.

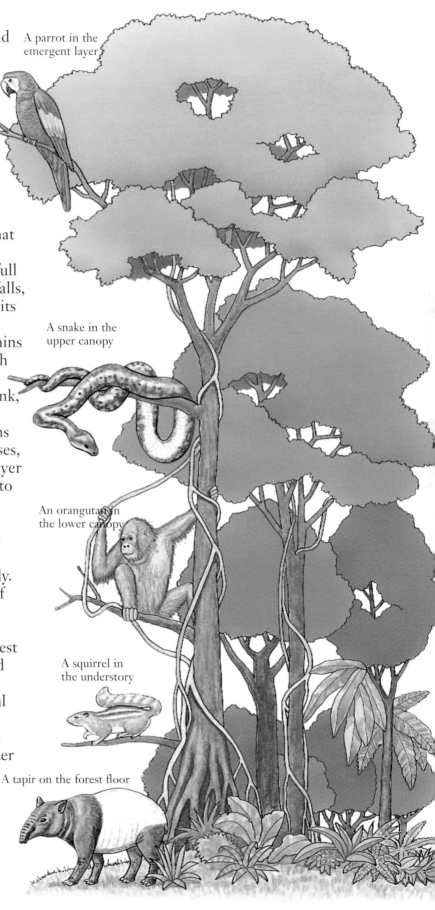

A parrot in the emergent layer

A snake in the upper canopy

An orangutan in the lower canopy

A squirrel in the understory

A tapir on the forest floor

Fossil

Any evidence of past life preserved in the rocks of Earth's crust

Fossils (FAH-suhlz) are the remains or traces of living organisms that died long ago but have been preserved in rocks. They vary in size from tiny traces that can be seen only with a microscope, to the skeletons of giant mammals and dinosaurs. Fossils provide fascinating evidence of living things that existed on Earth millions of years ago. The study of fossils is called paleontology, and scientists who work in this area are called paleontologists.

Around 2,500 years ago, the ancient Greeks were the first to realize that fossils were the remains of once-living things. During the Middle Ages (500–1500 C.E.), many people thought fossils were the work of the Devil. It was not until the late 18th century that fossils were widely recognized for what they are.

Most fossils are found in layers of sedimentary (SEH-duh-MEN-tuh-ree) rocks that formed thousands or millions of years ago. These are rocks formed of grains or fragments of mud, sand, or gravel, which were mostly laid down on the bed of seas, lakes or rivers, and were later compressed (packed down) to form hard rock. Fossils are also found preserved in tar, peat, ice, and amber.

Fossils provide clues about the ancient history of our planet, including the history of Earth's rocks, seas, and climate. Scientists use fossils to divide Earth's distant past into eras or ages, each of which lasted millions of years. Fossils also provide evidence of the origins of life on Earth, and the habits of creatures that died out long ago. In general, fossils support the theory of

A fossilized skull of an ichthyosaur (marine reptile). The first complete skeleton was excavated by Mary Anning (1799–1847). Her work helped to popularize fossil collecting.

HIGHLIGHTS

◆ Fossils are the evidence of past life on Earth, preserved in rocks. The oldest fossils date back to Precambrian times more than 570 million years ago, when living things evolved.

◆ Fossils help scientists to reconstruct Earth's ancient history. They provide a record of evolution and an indication of the climate millions of years ago. Fossils can also be used to sequence rocks.

◆ There are three main types of fossils: body, trace, and chemical fossils. Most fossils are body fossils. These are mainly the hard parts of once-living creatures, such as bones, shells, and teeth.

evolution, which suggests that over time, living things change and adapt in order to become better suited to the conditions in which they live. The idea of evolution was first put forward by British naturalist Charles Darwin (1809–1882) in the mid-19th century.

Types of fossils

There are many different types of fossils. They range from forests of fossilized tree stumps to insects preserved in amber and whole mammoths freeze-dried in permanently frozen soil. Coral reefs and footprints left by prehistoric animals are also fossils. Most fossils fall into one of three main categories: chemical fossils, trace fossils, and body fossils.

Chemical fossils

Chemical fossil material such as coal, oil, and gas are formed from the remains of once-living organisms. They are called fossil fuels. Coal is the carbon from fossil plants buried thousands of feet down among layers of sedimentary rock. Oil and gas probably come from the decomposition of marine creatures. The energy in these fossil fuels was gathered by organisms millions of years ago and it is now released when the fuels are burned.

Trace fossils

Trace fossils can provide an amazing record of the behavior of creatures in the distant past. As their name suggests, these are the fossilized signs or traces of animals, plants, or other living organisms. They include ancient footprints and animal burrows. For example, millions of years ago, worms lived in burrows that they tunnelled in the soft sand or mud of ancient seabeds. Different types of worms dug burrows with different shapes and patterns. Later, when the creatures died, these hollow tubes filled up with fresh sediment. The shape of the original burrow became preserved when the sediments

Human Fossils

LOOK CLOSER The topic of human evolution has been controversial since naturalist Charles Darwin first proposed it in the mid-19th century. Only 150 years ago, many people were outraged at the idea that humans could have evolved from apes.

However, in the last few decades, scientists have shown that the genes (JEENZ; strands of deoxyribonucleic acid, often called DNA, that carry inherited characteristics) of the higher apes, such as chimpanzees and gorillas, are very similar to human genes. There is now no doubt that the nearest living relatives of humans are bonobo chimpanzees. Moreover, humans and some apes shared a common ancestor a mere five million years ago.

Fossils of early humans and apes provide evidence of our evolution. Fossils found in east Africa give a good idea of human evolution over the last 15 million years. The first human ancestors to walk upright lived around 3.6 million years ago. U.S. anthropologist Don Johanson found a partial skeleton of an australopithecine in Ethiopia in 1973, which he nicknamed Lucy. Modern humans of the genus (JEE-nuhs; group) *Homo*, to which today's humans belong, first evolved in Africa 2.4 million years ago and later spread around the world.

hardened to form rock. Such fossilized burrows are often all that survives of the worms of the distant past, but they can be crucial to the picture of Earth's history. Today, marine worms are common in intertidal mudflats, and many early Cambrian rocks, with worm burrow fossils, are interpreted as forming in this environment.

Trace fossils also include evidence of much larger creatures than worms. Dinosaur footprints are quite common. Whole sets of tracks show that some plant-eating dinosaurs lived and moved around in herds, just as many plant-eating mammals do today. This evidence tell scientists about the behavior of animals they will never see.

Early human footprints were found in 1978 at Laetoli in Tanzania, east Africa. The footprints were left by apelike creatures called australopithecines (aw-STRAH-loh-PIH-thuh-

SYNZ) 3.6 million years ago. The pattern of tracks shows that two of them walked side by side, while smaller members of the group followed in their steps, carefully treading in the larger prints.

The prints at Laetoli were laid down during a volcanic eruption. The group was walking away from the eruption, crossing a layer of warm ash deposited on the floor of a river valley. Later, the river washed mud into and over the prints. The ash slowly hardened to form a rock called tuff, while the mud hardened into shale. These footprints are the earliest evidence of human ancestors walking upright as people do today, rather than ambling along as apes do.

Body fossils

Most fossils are body fossils. These are parts of living organisms that have been preserved in sediments and rocks. Most often, only the hard parts of the living things, such as shells, bones, and teeth, survive to become embedded in mud, sand, peat, or tar. The softer parts rot away.

Body fossils vary from tiny shells and the eggs of ancient birds and dinosaurs, to skeletons and even preserved bodies. An entire baby mammoth, nicknamed Dima, was found in permanently frozen soil in arctic Russia in 1977. Mammoths were ancient members of the elephant family that became extinct around 10,000 years ago. Dima

lived and died about 40,000 years ago. Body fossils may be almost unchanged from the time they were laid down, or the organic (plant or animal) material may have been replaced by minerals. Such remains are mineralized fossils.

Only a tiny proportion of living things survive to become fossils. However, certain types of fossils are relatively common because the living organisms existed in conditions where their remains were much more likely to be preserved. Such conditions prevail in the shallow seas that edge the coasts of continents. Some of the most common fossils are the remains of shelled sea creatures, such as ancient mollusks called ammonites, that lived in these coastal waters.

How fossils are preserved

The chances of all or part of a living organism being fossilized are quite slim. Most animals that die in the wild are eaten before they can be buried under sand, mud, or some other material that will preserve them. If the remains are not broken up and scattered by other animals, then decay, weathering and other natural processes destroy much of the body. Only the toughest parts, such as the shells and teeth, are left because they are the hardest to eat and the most resistant to decay.

Next, sedimentation is likely to damage and scatter the remains that have survived so far. On the beds of seas, lakes, and rivers, the bits and pieces are worn, broken, and tossed about by water currents before being buried under sediment. They are then squashed as the layers of sediment that have built up over them turn to rock.

Later, movements of Earth's crust (outer layer) may slowly raise the beds

Geologists can tell this rock was formed in the sea in the Jurassic period because of the ammonite fossils that it contains.

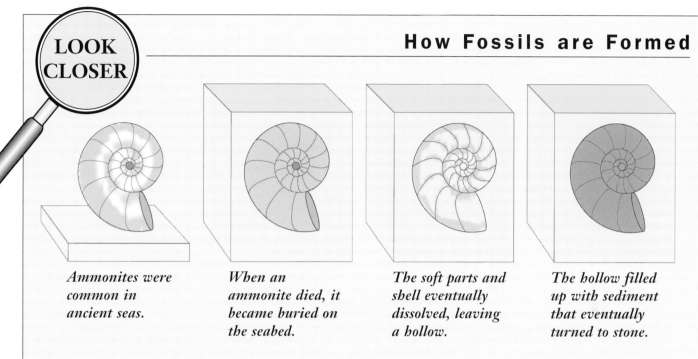

LOOK CLOSER

How Fossils are Formed

Ammonites were common in ancient seas.

When an ammonite died, it became buried on the seabed.

The soft parts and shell eventually dissolved, leaving a hollow.

The hollow filled up with sediment that eventually turned to stone.

Fossils are formed in a number of different ways. The diagram above shows the formation of an ammonite fossil. Ammonites were shelled sea creatures related to squids and octopuses. When the ammonite died, it sank to the seabed and was buried under sand or mud. The soft body of the creature rotted, leaving the hard shell. Over millions of years, more layers of sediment settled on top of the shell. Eventually, the shell dissolved, leaving a hollow. The hollow formed a mold. Fresh sediment filled it and eventually turned to rock. The new rock formed a cast that exactly matched the shape of the original creature.

Other fossils are preserved in amber, the remains of sticky tree resin that has hardened. When an insect such as a fly landed on the resin oozing down the bark of a tree in an ancient forest, it became trapped and died. The resin hardened and was preserved when the rest of the tree rotted away. Fossils preserved in amber are quite common and are often used to make beautiful jewelry.

of shallow seas so that they become dry land. Some sedimentary rocks are preserved in cliffs on the edge of modern oceans. Later still, natural processes such as wind, rain, or the pounding of the waves expose the layers of rocks that contain fossils. Fossil-bearing rocks may also come to light as rock is excavated in quarries or mines, or during the construction of new roads or towns.

On land, there is little chance of a whole creature being buried by natural processes. Only where there has been a sudden catastrophe such as a flood, or where an animal has fallen into water, do the remains stand much chance of being preserved. Most land surfaces are constantly being worn away by weathering by the elements, and as sediments are washed away by streams and rivers. Only where there is a natural sediment trap, such as a valley or depression in

the land, can sediment build up to such depths that it cannot afterward be worn away.

The Great Rift Valley in east Africa is an example of a sediment trap: a wide, flat-bottomed valley that formed as the land on either side rose up as a result of movements of Earth's crust. The Rift Valley contains the world's best-preserved fossil record of early human ancestors and the world in which they lived. In North America, large sediment basins formed on the flanks of the Rocky Mountains as they were lifted up during Mesozoic times, between 245 and 66.4 million years ago. The rocks there contain the remains of dinosaurs that dominated the area at the time.

CHECK THESE OUT!
✔CONTINENTAL SHELF ✔EXTINCTION ✔GEOLOGIC TIMESCALE ✔PLATE TECTONICS ✔SEDIMENTARY ROCK

Friction

The force that reduces the slipperiness between two surfaces is called friction. Without friction, everyday activities such as walking and cycling would be impossible. Friction provides the grip, or the push against the ground, that lets humans and animals walk without falling. Friction also allows automobiles to accelerate, brake, and steer. Friction between moving parts in engines reduces their power output, but this loss can be kept to a minimum by lubrication using oil or grease.

Causes of friction

Even the smoothest of surfaces are full of microscopic pits and bumps. When two surfaces rub together, only a small fraction of their surface areas are in contact because of these pits and bumps. The pressure at these points can be huge. Atoms in the two surfaces start to attract and repel one another almost as if they were part of a single object.

When the two surfaces move relative to one another, for example, if a book is pushed across the surface of a desk, attractions between the atoms in the two surfaces have to be overcome. There is a resistance to motion between two surfaces in contact.

Making and breaking bonds between the atoms in two surfaces increases the energy with which those atoms vibrate. This increased vibration is a form of heat energy, and most of the work carried out to overcome friction is changed to heat. Friction therefore produces heat.

Some energy is changed to sound, such as squeaky wheels that need oiling. Electrons are sometimes removed from one surface and held in the other, so both surfaces become charged with static electricity and some of the work against friction becomes electrical energy.

HIGHLIGHTS

♦ Friction is caused by attractive forces between two surfaces in contact.

♦ The frictional force between surfaces that are not moving relative to each other can be greater than the force between moving surfaces.

♦ Lubricants reduce friction by keeping moving surfaces apart.

♦ Rolling friction is a form of friction that affects wheeled vehicles.

Friction is strongest just before two touching objects begin relative motion because the objects are in good contact with one another. Once one object starts to move, the frictional force falls. The attractions between moving surfaces are weaker than those between still surfaces, so the frictional force is less. Lubricants reduce friction by forming a layer between the surfaces and preventing them from being in direct contact.

The coefficient of friction

The size of the frictional force between two surfaces is proportional to the force that holds them together. If the force doubles, so does the friction. If the force acts at an angle to the surface, only the part of the force that acts at right angles to the surface (called the normal force) has an effect on friction. The frictional force does not depend on the area of the surfaces in contact, as a larger surface area spreads out the normal force, reducing pressure between surfaces. In the case of two nonmoving surfaces, the type of friction involved is called static friction. The coefficient of static friction depends on what materials each of the two surfaces are made of.

If a book is pulled across a surface by a string, the force on the string must be greater than the static frictional force for the book to start moving. Once the book is moving, less force is needed to keep it moving steadily because a different coefficient of friction applies, which is called the coefficient of kinetic friction. The coefficient of kinetic friction is less than the coefficient of static friction for a given combination of surfaces.

The coefficient of friction between the sole of a shoe and

A skier uses friction between her skis and the snow to make a turn. Otherwise she would continue in a straight line.

LOOK CLOSER

Fluid Friction

Friction is not confined to vehicles that travel on land. Ships have to overcome friction when they pass through water. The water molecules (MAH-lih-KYOOLZ; atoms bonded together) must slide past one another to make room for the ship. Resistance to this motion is a type of internal friction called viscosity (vis-KAH-suh-tee). The water also rubs against the surface of a ship as it moves. The frictional force is proportional to the surface area of the hull below water and the ship's length. Barnacles and other organisms that stick to the hull can make its surface rough, increasing the coefficient of friction and increasing the amount of fuel used by the ship. Many ship hulls are sandblasted to remove barnacles and coated with antifouling paint, which poisons organisms that try to attach themselves to the hull.

floor surfaces must be at least 0.2 to prevent slips. The coefficient of friction between an automobile tire and a dry road surface is much higher—around 0.8—allowing for rapid braking and acceleration. This drops to 0.5 on a wet road or 0.1 on an icy road.

Rolling friction

Rolling friction is caused when the load on two surfaces in contact slightly compresses (squeezes) the surfaces. A certain amount of energy is needed to make a surface deform in this way. This energy can come from a vehicle's engine. A pneumatic tire's rolling friction depends on its air pressure. If the tire's pressure is correct, the tire deforms little and the rolling friction is kept to a minimum.

The metal wheels of a train hardly deform at all, so the rolling friction is less that that of an automobile tire. However, the combination of metal wheels and metal rails means a low static friction. This is why trains have to accelerate more gently and brake over greater distances than automobiles.

CHECK THESE OUT!
✔ENERGY ✔FORCE ✔HEAT

Fusion

Joining together small atoms to make larger atoms and produce energy

Almost all the world's energy comes from the Sun. The Sun itself releases energy by joining together small atoms to make larger ones. This process is called fusion (FYOO-zhuhn). Scientists know how to use fusion to make powerful nuclear weapons but are unsure of how to make fusion happen in full-scale power plants.

Physics of fusion

All atoms (the building blocks of chemical elements) are made from smaller particles called protons, neutrons, and electrons. Protons and neutrons are clumped together to make the nucleus (NOO-klee-uhs; center) of the atom. The electrons spin around the nucleus. The simplest atom, hydrogen, has one proton and one electron. The next simplest, helium, has two protons and two electrons. It should be possible, therefore, to make helium by joining together (fusing) two hydrogen atoms. However, because helium also contains two neutrons, it can be made only from a heavy type of hydrogen called deuterium (doo-TIR-ee-uhm), which contains one proton, one neutron, and one electron.

Three different nuclear reactions are needed to change hydrogen into helium. First, two atoms of hydrogen minus their electrons (in other words, two protons) combine to form deuterium.

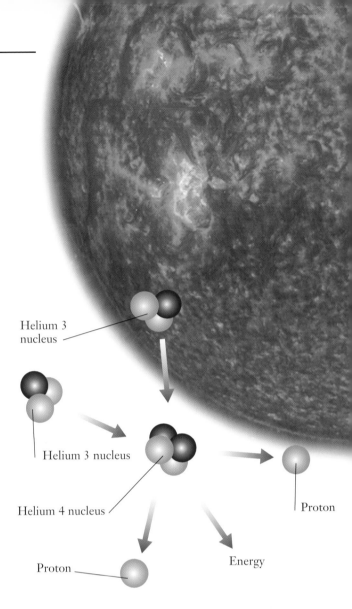

In the process of fusion, two helium 3 nuclei fuse to form a helium 4 nucleus, two protons, and a lot of energy. This process happens constantly in the Sun.

Next, the deuterium reacts with more hydrogen to produce an unstable type of helium. Finally, two of these unstable helium atoms join to form the stable type of helium, plus two protons. The protons can kick-start the process over again, producing a chain reaction.

When nuclei are formed by fusion, energy is given off. Fusion occurs because the protons and neutrons can form a more stable (lower energy) arrangement by combining to form a single nucleus. The extra energy is released as heat or light. Fusion does not occur readily because the positively charged nuclei repel each other. They must therefore collide violently, at high temperature, to get close enough for the required rearrangement. Each of the three reactions

---

HIGHLIGHTS

◆ The Sun's energy is produced by nuclear fusion that turns hydrogen into helium.

◆ Fusion (joining atoms together) can produce much more energy than fission (splitting atoms apart).

◆ Scientists have not yet made fusion happen reliably enough to build a full-scale fusion plant.

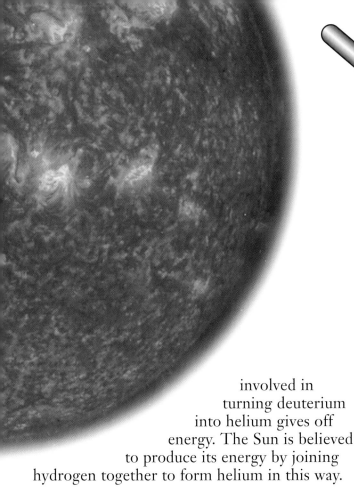

LOOK CLOSER

Inside a Reactor

A fusion reactor, the apparatus in which nuclear fusion takes place, tries to produce conditions almost like those on the Sun. Very high temperatures turn the deuterium atoms used in fusion into a type of exploded gas called a plasma. However, plasma is so hot that no normal container could hold it without melting. Physicists therefore developed a magnetic bottle. Just as glass holds liquid in a bottle, so magnetic fields are used to trap plasma in a cylinder of space like the inside of a tin can. This did not work because the plasma could escape from the open ends. The scientists therefore joined the ends to produce a donut shape called a torus. Some fusion reactors use tokamaks (torus-shaped chambers inside magnetic fields) to produce extremely high temperatures. Other reactors use lasers to heat tiny pellets of deuterium to immensely high temperatures for short periods of time. So far, neither tokamaks nor laser fusion have produced useful amounts of energy.

involved in turning deuterium into helium gives off energy. The Sun is believed to produce its energy by joining hydrogen together to form helium in this way.

Fusion bombs

Fusion is not the only way to produce nuclear energy. During World War II (1939–1945), U.S. physicists managed to carry out nuclear fission (FIH-shuhn). This process produces energy by splitting large atoms into smaller and more stable atoms. Fission was used to produce the first nuclear bombs, but scientists soon realized fusion could produce more energy and more powerful bombs. They set about trying to make a bomb that could recreate the powerful nuclear reactions taking place in the Sun.

The main problem was how to recreate on Earth the very high temperatures of the Sun. The scientists realized they would need to use a fission bomb to reach the high temperatures needed for fusion. In November 1952, the United States successfully detonated (exploded) the first fusion bomb at Eniwetok Atoll in the South Pacific. It was called a hydrogen bomb (or thermonuclear bomb because it involves both heat and nuclear energy). The hydrogen bomb produced a blast equivalent to 10 million tons (9 million tonnes) of high-explosive TNT. Soon afterward, scientists from the Soviet Union produced a bomb 10 times more powerful.

Energy from fusion

Making nuclear energy by splitting uranium and plutonium atoms using nuclear fission also produces highly dangerous radioactive waste. Fusion does not produce this waste and, because it can release up to 10 times more energy than fission, should be a better way of producing nuclear power. Fusion has many other benefits too. Unlike fission, which relies on rare and expensive uranium, the raw ingredient of fusion is deuterium, which is made from ordinary water. It has been estimated that there is enough deuterium in the oceans to make all the energy that people will ever need.

Scientists had to achieve immensely high temperatures to make the hydrogen bomb. These temperatures are required inside fusion reactors. Achieving this has proved extremely difficult, and despite nearly 50 years of research, the world is still without a single nuclear fusion power plant.

CHECK THESE OUT!
✔ATOM ✔FISSION ✔HYDROGEN
✔ISOTOPE ✔NUCLEAR PHYSICS ✔SUN

Galaxy

Huge collection of stars, gas, and dust, separated by light-years of empty space

Collections of many millions of stars and clouds of gas and dust pulled together by their own gravity are called galaxies. Most galaxies are so large that light takes thousands of years to cross them. Galaxies float in space, separated from neighboring galaxies by millions of light-years (one light-year is approximately 6 trillion miles or 10 trillion km), yet sometimes they collide. Galaxies are held together in large groups called galaxy clusters and superclusters.

Types of galaxies

No two galaxies are the same. Astronomers group them into several different types, each with their own properties and histories. Galaxies may be spirals, barred spirals, ellipticals, irregulars, or lenticulars.

Spiral galaxies are flattened disks of stars, gas, and dust, with a bright bulge at their center and two or more spiral arms leading out from the center to the edge of the disk. The spiral arms are constantly changing, revolving around the center as the galaxy rotates over hundreds of millions of years. They show up because they contain the brightest and youngest stars in the

Two spiral galaxies pass by each other in this picture taken by the Hubble Space Telescope.

HIGHLIGHTS

♦ Galaxies are the only places in the Universe where stars are made.

♦ There are different types of galaxies—ellipticals, spirals, barred spirals, irregulars, and lenticulars.

galaxy. Older stars are found in the galaxy's center and scattered in the space between the arms. Spirals are all about the same size.

Barred spirals have a bar of stars running across the middle of the galaxy, joining the bulge to the spiral arms. Earth's Milky Way galaxy is a typical spiral galaxy, containing 100 billion stars in a disk about 100,000 light-years across.

Elliptical galaxies are balls of stars with shapes varying from spheres to elongated ovals. All these different shapes are ellipses (ih-LIP-seez). Ellipticals (ih-LIP-tih-kuhlz) contain little gas or dust to form new stars. They are made mostly of very old stars. Astronomers think they are the oldest type of galaxy in the Universe. Ellipticals vary in size. Giant ones are over two million light-years across and are cannibals. They grow by pulling in and absorbing surrounding galaxies.

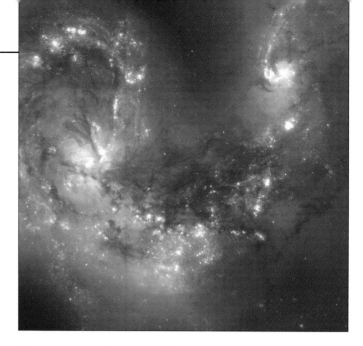

Some small galaxies have no apparent structure and contain large amounts of gas, dust, and young stars. These are called irregular galaxies and include the Large and Small Magellanic Clouds that orbit the Milky Way.

Lenticular galaxies are lens-shaped galaxies, which are a cross between spiral and irregular types. They contain large amounts of dust but little gas. The gas seems to have been torn off in collisions with other galaxies because lenticulars are usually found in large galaxy clusters.

Lives of galaxies

Galaxies are the only places in the Universe where enough gas and dust collect to create stars. They must have begun forming long before the first stars started to shine. Today, galaxies are crowded together in clusters and superclusters with huge voids (VOYDZ) of empty space between them. These superclusters and voids are the largest structures in the Universe.

Material inside these clusters and superclusters was pulled together to make individual galaxies. Some astronomers think that galaxies were

Two spiral galaxies collide. The cores of the galaxies are orange. Several blue stars have been created.

pulled together by huge black holes with powerful gravity (force) that gathered gas and dust around them.

Violent galaxies

The black hole theory can explain why some galaxies seem to have very violent lives. When astronomers look into space they look back in time because the light from distant galaxies can travel only 6 trillion miles (10 trillion km) a year. Astronomers can therefore see galaxies around eight billion light-years away as they actually appeared shortly after the Universe was created. These galaxies are called quasars (KWAY-zahrz). They release huge amounts of energy from their cores, which astronomers think is produced as a giant black hole at the quasar's center swallows up material from the surrounding region.

Some other, much closer galaxies are also releasing more energy than expected. These active galaxies include radio galaxies, which have jets of hot material bursting out on either side of their cores, and Seyfert galaxies, which look like normal spiral galaxies but have much brighter central regions. Astronomers think these galaxies also contain black holes. Some think every galaxy has a black hole at its center and passes through an active phase at some time in its life.

CHECK THESE OUT!
✔COSMOLOGY ✔MILKY WAY
✔QUASAR✔SPACE ✔STAR ✔UNIVERSE

STORY OF SCIENCE

Edwin Hubble and Galaxies

Until the 1920s, no one realized there were other galaxies outside the Milky Way. Astronomers had discovered that the sky was full of small, faint clouds of light called nebulas (NEH-byuh-luhz). There was no way to measure their distance, however, so no one could tell how big they were. In the 1920s, U.S. astronomer Edwin Hubble (1889–1953) discovered that some of the nebulas contained variable stars (stars that regularly change their brightness) that were identical to stars in the Milky Way, only far fainter. The stars always had the same brightness, so they had to be millions of light-years away, far beyond the edges of the Milky Way.

Hubble also realized that the galaxies were not all spirals—the clouds of light had many different forms. He invented the system of classification (grouping) that is still used today and went on to discover that all the galaxies in the Universe are moving away from each other. In other words, the Universe is expanding.

Gas

The three forms of matter are solid, liquid, and gas. The particles in solids arrange themselves in tight, rigid structures that do not change shape easily. In liquids, the particles are also close together but they can slip past one another with ease. Liquids can therefore change shape to fill the bottom of a container. The particles in a gas spread much farther apart and can fill the whole of a container, rather than grouping together as the particles in solids and liquids do. Gases have no fixed volume or shape.

Kinetic theory

Before scientists discovered that gases consist of atoms and molecules moving around in space, the only way to relate the pressure of a gas to its volume and temperature was by measuring these three properties and plotting graphs of how they varied. The results of these studies are the gas laws, which are simple equations relating temperature, pressure, and volume. Once scientists realized that gases were composed of tiny particles (molecules or atoms) in rapid motion, they were able to interpret the pressure and temperature of a gas in terms of the average speed and number of molecules, thus explaining the gas law equations. This explanation is called the kinetic theory of gases.

The particles in a gas move rapidly at an average speed that increases with temperature. Imagine a single gas particle trapped in a container and moving at that average speed. From time to time, the gas particle will collide with a wall of the container and bounce back at the same speed until it hits

HIGHLIGHTS
◆ Gases have no fixed volume or shape.
◆ Gases cannot be liquefied by pressure alone; vapors can be liquefied under pressure.
◆ The volume of a gas is inversely proportional to its pressure and directly proportional to its temperature on the absolute scale.
◆ The noble gases are chemical elements that rarely react with other elements.

The behavior of the bubbles from a deep-sea diver shows how gases are much less dense (closely packed) than liquids and will always float to the surface.

another wall. In a smaller box, the particle will collide with the walls more often because it has less distance to travel between them.

The pressure on the walls of a gas's container results from constant collisions with vast

STORY OF SCIENCE

The Gas Laws

In the 17th and 18th centuries, certain scientists were studying the properties of gases. They were particularly interested in the relationship between the pressure, volume, and temperature of a sample of gas. One of the pioneers of the gas laws was Irish-born scientist Robert Boyle (1627–1691). In 1662, Boyle observed that the volume of a sample of gas halves if its pressure doubles without the temperature changing. Put another way, multiplying the pressure of a gas by its volume always gives the same result for a given sample of gas at a given temperature. The mathematical expression of Boyle's law is pV = constant, where p is pressure, V is volume, and the constant is a number that depends on the amount of gas and its temperature.

In 1787, French scientist Jacques Charles (1746–1823) studied the relationship between the temperature and the volume of a gas. Being a keen balloonist, Charles knew that a gas became less dense when heated, which is the effect that makes hot-air balloons rise. He measured the volumes of gas samples at different temperatures and found that the volume of a gas expands by 1/273 its starting volume for every 1.8°F (1°C) increase in temperature. When Charles plotted graphs of volume against temperature, he found that every line reached zero volume at the same temperature: –460°F (–273°C). This temperature is now called absolute zero. The absolute scale measures temperature in kelvin (K) and starts at 0K (–460°F; –273°C). The freezing point of water, 32°F (0°C), is 273K on the absolute scale. By Charles's law, the volume of a sample of gas at constant pressure is proportional to its temperature, T, on the absolute scale: V = constant x T.

The combination of Boyle's law (pV = constant) and Charles's law (V = constant x T) is called the ideal gas law: pV = constant x T. The constant depends on the amount of gas in the sample.

Doubling the amount of gas in a fixed volume at a given temperature will double the pressure. This is why the ideal gas law is most often written pV = nRT, where n is a measure of the number of atoms or molecules in the sample. R is the universal gas constant, which has the same value for any ideal gas.

Different welding methods (used to join metals) use different gases. In gas-shielded arc welding, a gas such as argon, helium, or carbon dioxide is used to shield the welding from oxygen in the air. As a result the join is stronger.

numbers of gas particles. If the volume of the container is reduced, each particle hits the wall more often and so the pressure rises. If the temperature increases, the particles move faster. Moving faster makes the particles hit the walls more often and harder, which also increases the pressure. The kinetic theory of gases calculates the pressure of a gas using Newton's laws of motion. The result is called the ideal gas law, which agrees with and describes the experimental results for most gases.

The calculations of simple kinetic theory are based on the assumption that the particles in a gas are so widely spaced and fast moving that they never collide with each other. This assumption holds well for gases that are far above their boiling points. It works less well at high pressures or at low temperatures, when the gas is close to becoming liquid. The gas particles are closer together and start to feel the effects of forces that attract them to each other. Under these conditions, the pressure of the gas is lower than predicted by the ideal gas law equation. This is called nonideal behavior.

Gases and vapors

In everyday language, the terms gas and vapor are often used to describe the same things. In scientific language, there is a difference between the two states. A gas never turns into a liquid, no matter how much it is compressed, as long as the temperature does not change. This is because its

particles move so quickly that they escape the forces of attraction that would otherwise make them liquefy or solidify. Below a certain temperature, called the critical temperature, most gases become vapors. The vapors will become liquid if they are compressed.

Imagine a sample of vapor in a cylinder with a close-fitting piston. If the cylinder is large enough, the vapor will behave just like a gas at low pressure. As the piston is pushed into the cylinder, the pressure will increase, as Boyle's gas law predicts (see the box on page 293). At a certain point, however, the pressure will stay the same, even though the piston is pushed farther into the cylinder. This is the vapor pressure of the liquid. When the pressure of a vapor reaches this value, it starts to turn into a liquid. As the piston is pushed farther into the cylinder, more of the vapor liquefies. Because liquid occupies a fraction of the space that a gas would occupy, the pressure does not rise until all the vapor has turned into liquid. Then, because liquids are much harder to compress than gases, the pressure rises steeply if the piston is pushed farther into the cylinder. Withdrawing the piston reverses the process and the liquid turns into vapor.

Diffusion

Diffusion is the movement of matter from a region of high concentration, or pressure, to a region of low concentration. Imagine a cylinder full of gas connected to an empty cylinder

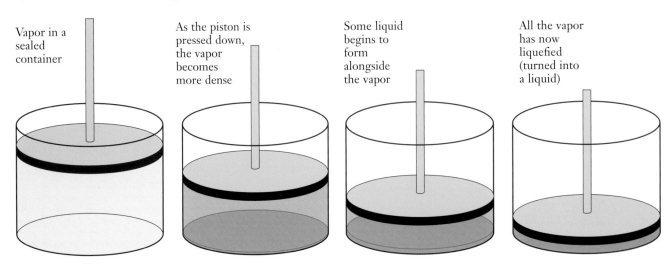

Vapor in a sealed container

As the piston is pressed down, the vapor becomes more dense

Some liquid begins to form alongside the vapor

All the vapor has now liquefied (turned into a liquid)

If a vapor inside a piston is compressed at constant temperature, it will begin to liquefy. The pressure will remain constant while both liquid and vapor are present.

EVERYDAY SCIENCE

The Noble Gases

Helium, neon, argon, krypton, xenon, and radon are called the noble gases, the elements that form group 18 (0) of the periodic table. Noble gases are sometimes called inert gases because they rarely form compounds with other elements. Helium, neon, and argon form no compounds at all. Incandescent lamps—bulbs that contain a finely coiled filament that glows when switched on—are usually filled with argon, which prevents the filament from burning away. This is because argon does not react with the metal of the filament, even at white heat, unlike oxygen, for example, which would help the filament burn.

A discharge tube is another form of lighting that uses noble gases. Discharge tubes are often called neon lights, but they can also use argon or krypton instead of neon. These sealed glass tubes contain noble gases at very low pressure. When a current passes between the two electrodes of a discharge tube, it takes electrons out of the noble gas atoms. These electrons then carry an electrical current through the tube. This process causes the noble gas to glow. True neon tubes glow bright red, but they can be made to glow other colors by coating the insides of the tubes with chemicals.

Neon, argon, or krypton fill the tubes of neon lights and make them glow along with electricity.

through a tap. If the tap is opened, gas will flow from the full cylinder into the empty cylinder until both cylinders are at the same pressure. This is because the open tap lets gas particles pass through it, rather than bouncing them back into the full cylinder. The gas diffuses from the full cylinder to fill both cylinders evenly. As the pressures in the two cylinders become equal, the number of particles passing between the cylinders is the same in both directions, so the pressures remain equal. If the two cylinders contain two different gases, opening the tap allows the two gases to diffuse into each other so that the mixture becomes even throughout.

British chemist Thomas Graham (1805–1869) studied the diffusion of gases. He measured the speed at which different gases diffused through a porous barrier. A porous barrier has tiny channels that lead from one side of the barrier to the other. Graham found that the rate of diffusion of a gas is inversely proportional to the square root of its density. In other words, if a gas called A is four times as dense as a gas called B,

gas B will diffuse twice as quickly as gas A through the porous barrier.

The nuclear fuel industry uses diffusion to enrich uranium fuel. Natural uranium contains less than one percent U^{235}, the radioactive isotope. The rest is U^{238}, which is not radioactive. To make useful fuel, the proportion of U^{235} must be increased. First, the gas uranium hexafluoride (UF_6) is made. Molecules of $U^{235}F_6$ are slightly lighter than molecules of $U^{238}F_6$, so they diffuse through a porous barrier slightly faster. If a mixture of $U^{235}F_6$ and $U^{238}F_6$ is passed through a porous barrier, the first part of the mixture contains slightly more $U^{235}F_6$ than the original mixture. After thousands of repeated diffusions, the mixture contains up to 3 percent $U^{235}F_6$, which is then changed into uranium for making nuclear fuel.

CHECK THESE OUT!
✔ATMOSPHERE ✔CARBON DIOXIDE
✔CHEMISTRY ✔FORCE ✔NEWTONIAN PHYSICS
✔OXYGEN ✔TEMPERATURE

Gemini Mission

Two-person space flights that paved the way for the Apollo Moon landings

The first step into space for the United States was the Mercury program. This series of missions from 1961 to 1963 carried single astronauts into space for short flights in orbit around Earth. The Mercury space capsules were very light because the United States' rockets at the time were much less powerful than those used by the then Soviet Union (Russia). More powerful rockets had enabled the Soviet Union to open up a lead in the space race, putting the first artificial satellites and astronauts in space ahead of the United States. The Gemini program put two-person spacecraft into orbit for much longer periods, allowing the U.S. National Aeronautics and Space Administration (NASA) to catch up with the Soviet Union and eventually to overtake it in the race for the Moon.

The Gemini program was made up of two unpiloted and ten piloted flights, launched between April 1964 and November 1966. The missions tested many of the complicated tasks that were later used in the Apollo Moon flights.

The Gemini spacecraft

Unlike today's space shuttles, the Gemini spacecraft was designed to be used once and then thrown away. Each Gemini was launched into space on top of a *Titan II* rocket. Gemini itself was a three-part spacecraft. It had a reentry module, a retrograde module, and an equipment module. Of these, only the reentry module returned to Earth.

The reentry module was a cone-shaped capsule where the astronauts lived in cramped conditions for flights lasting several days. Even though Gemini carried two people (the Gemini program was named after a constellation that represents a set of twins from Greek and Roman legends), the capsule was only 50 percent bigger than the one-person vehicle used in the Mercury program. The astronauts sat in ejector seats in the middle of the capsule with hatches over their heads. They were surrounded by the instruments and equipment they would need during the flight. At the top of the cone was a cylinder-shaped docking device that allowed the spacecraft to attach itself to other vehicles in space.

The bottom of the cone was a shield built to withstand the tremendous heat built up as the reentry module fell back to Earth. Once Earth's atmosphere had slowed the fall of the capsule, parachutes were released so that it drifted gently back to splash down in the sea.

The retrograde module was a ring of engines and fuel tanks attached to the base of the cone. Six rocket nozzles in a circle around the module could be fired, allowing the spacecraft to steer in different directions and change its orbit. Gemini was the first spacecraft that could steer. This was a very important step in the history of space exploration. The module got its name because it contained four retro-rockets that slowed down the spacecraft and lowered its orbit when the time came to return to Earth.

Behind the retrograde module came the equipment module, carrying the equipment to which the astronauts did not need direct access. This included the astronauts' air and water tanks, electricity generators to heat and light the capsule, and small thrusters to adjust the angle of the spacecraft during flight.

HIGHLIGHTS

♦ The Gemini spacecraft were two-person capsules developed from the earlier Mercury program.

♦ The first crewed Gemini mission was launched in March 1965.

♦ Astronaut Edward White became the first U.S. spacewalker during the flight of *Gemini 4*.

Early missions

The Gemini launches started with probing missions to test the technology involved. Over the course of the 10 crewed launches, the missions became more and more complex. *Gemini 1* and *Gemini 2* were uncrewed test-firing missions. *Gemini 1* was simply a test that the spacecraft would work with the *Titan II* rocket launcher. The spacecraft was not even separated from the rocket. *Gemini 2* put a Gemini spacecraft into space for the first time, on a suborbital flight that quickly brought it back to Earth from a height of around 100 miles (160 km). This test was designed to check that the retrograde section rockets worked and could safely return the reentry module to Earth.

Gemini 3 (March 23, 1965) was the first piloted Gemini flight, crewed by astronauts Virgil "Gus" Grissom and John Young. Grissom had already been an astronaut in the Mercury program, and Young was a U.S. naval officer. Their mission was another cautious test. They stayed in orbit for less than five hours, but they still managed to carry out three scientific experiments and to photograph Earth from orbit. Using the retrograde module engines, they also changed the spacecraft's orbit, the first time this had been done.

Gemini 4 (June 3 to 7, 1965) was a five-day mission crewed by James McDivitt and Edward White. The highlight was Edward White's walk in space, the first by a U.S. astronaut.

Gemini 5 (August 21 to 29, 1965) was the longest space mission carried out by U.S. or Soviet astronauts until that time. Gordon Cooper and Charles Conrad were closely monitored during and after their eight-day mission. They proved it was possible for astronauts to stay in space long enough to reach the Moon and return, without any ill effects.

Docking in space

Gemini 6 was supposed to be the first U.S. spacecraft to meet up with another vessel in space, an uncrewed vehicle called *Agena*. *Gemini 6*'s crew were already on board and ready for launch when *Agena* exploded a short time after takeoff on October 5, 1965.

The launch of the uncrewed **Gemini 2** *space flight. This flight was a rehearsal for the crewed* **Gemini 3** *flight scheduled for 1965.*

STORY OF SCIENCE

The First U.S. Space Walk

Edward White's space walk was the highlight of the *Gemini 4* mission. The design of the Gemini reentry module, with hatches situated above the crew's seats, meant that both its astronauts had to put on their full spacesuits and the module had to be emptied of air before White could open the hatch and float into space.

White was attached to *Gemini 4* by a tether during his 20-minute space walk. He used a zip gun to move around in space. The gun fired short bursts of gas and acted just like a rocket. When the astronaut fired the gun in one direction, it pushed him the other way. It had only a small fuel tank, but White still managed two somersaults and two turns before it ran out. Called back into the spacecraft at the end of his space walk, White complained, "It's the saddest moment of my life."

NASA decided to solve the problem with an ambitious joint mission. The plan was that *Gemini 6* would meet up with its sister mission *Gemini 7* when that spacecraft was ready for launch in December 1965. However, *Gemini 7* was launched first, on December 4, 1965, and the astronauts had been in orbit for 11 days before *Gemini 6* was finally launched. The two spacecraft met up successfully. They made three orbits of Earth side by side, getting to within 1 foot (30 cm) of each other, although they did not actually dock (join up). After just 26 hours in space, *Gemini 6* returned to Earth on December 16, while *Gemini 7* came back two days later. The astronauts on board *Gemini 7* had set a new record by remaining in space for two weeks.

Gemini 8 (March 16 to 17, 1966) went a step further than *Gemini 6* and *Gemini 7*. This time, *Agena* reached orbit without any problem, and *Gemini 8*, piloted by Neil Armstrong (later the first person on the Moon) and David Scott, successfully docked with it. Unfortunately, the spacecraft began to roll due to a malfunction on board *Gemini 8*. The astronauts had to undock and return to Earth as a safety measure after less than 11 hours in space.

Later Gemini missions

Gemini 9 (June 3 to 6, 1966) was another space-docking mission that ran into problems. The target vehicle *Agena* again crashed without reaching orbit. This time NASA had a standby vehicle, called ATDA (augmented target docking adapter), ready to launch. But when *Gemini 9*'s astronauts, Thomas Stafford and Eugene Cernan, met up with ATDA, they found that part of the cover that had protected ATDA during launch had not come away properly. *Gemini 9* could not dock with it. The crew still practiced other tasks involved in docking, and Cernan took a two-hour space walk.

Gemini 10 (July 18 to 21, 1966) was much more successful. This time John Young and Michael Collins successfully docked their spacecraft with *Agena*. They used *Agena*'s engines to boost their orbit into an ellipse with a high point 475 miles (760 km) above Earth, the highest altitude reached by any astronauts up to this time. The Agena/Gemini combination then met up with *Agena 8* (the vehicle *Gemini 8* had docked with), and Collins took a space walk to recover a plate mounted on *Agena*'s side. This plate had been designed to collect

This photograph of the **Gemini 7** *spacecraft was taken through the hatch window of* **Gemini 6.**

This photograph of the Gemini 7 spacecraft was taken through the hatch window of Gemini 6.

LOOK CLOSER

Titan II Rocket

The *Titan II* rocket that launched Gemini was built as a long-range nuclear missile. It was able to carry a heavier payload (cargo) over greater distances than the Redstone and Atlas missiles that launched the Mercury spacecraft. *Titan II* also used different fuels from the earlier rockets, which were much easier to handle. The Atlas rocket used liquid oxygen, which boils at –297°F (–183°C), as part of its fuel mixture. All the fuels used for the Titan rocket were liquid at normal temperatures and did not need to be cooled. *Titan II* was also safer than the Mercury rockets because its fuel was less explosive. This allowed Gemini to carry ejection seats for its astronauts, which could blast them clear of the rocket in the event of an accident during launch. With an Atlas rocket the explosive charges in the ejector seats could have blown up the entire rocket.

Titan II was not used again for piloted missions after the Gemini program but it became an important launch vehicle for automatic satellites and spaceprobes. It is still in use today, mainly for launching U.S. spy satellites.

micrometeorites (very small specks of interplanetary dust) that could then be analyzed upon return to Earth.

Gemini 11 (September 12 to 15, 1966) and *Gemini 12* (November 11 to 15, 1966) were the final missions of the Gemini program. *Gemini 11*, piloted by Pete Conrad and Richard Gordon, practiced docking with an Agena vehicle and then carried out an experiment to make artificial gravity. The two spacecraft were tied together with a 98-foot (30-m) tether and set spinning around each other. The force created by this spinning movement produced a tiny amount of artificial gravity in *Gemini 11*'s cabin.

Gemini 12 was crewed by James Lovell and Edwin "Buzz" Aldrin (later the second man to walk on the Moon), who made three space walks and practiced using tools in space. The spacecraft made the first reentry automatically controlled from Earth.

Gemini's successes

The Gemini program achieved many space firsts for the United States and gave NASA the experience it needed to send astronauts to the Moon. Most important, Gemini proved that astronauts could survive in space for a week or

more—the time needed to get to the Moon and back—without any ill effects. The astronauts' hearts and blood circulations were monitored in space, and tests when they returned to Earth proved that weightlessness and radiation in space did not harm human blood.

Gemini tested most of the technology needed for the Apollo missions. The Gemini spacecraft changed orbits, docked with other vehicles in space, and traveled farther from Earth for longer than any previous piloted spacecraft. At the same time, the Soviet crewed space program ran into difficulties. The Soviet Union did not attempt any piloted launches during Gemini's lifetime. By the time the Soviet Union restarted their space program, NASA had opened up the lead that eventually put U.S. astronauts on the Moon.

CHECK THESE OUT!
✔APOLLO MISSION ✔MERCURY MISSION
✔MOON ✔NASA ✔SPACE

Gemstone

Mineral that is valued for its beauty when polished

Ruby, emerald, sapphire, and diamond are gemstones prized for their beauty and durability. They are usually rare and so are especially valuable. Many not-so-valuable minerals such as amethyst and cairngorm, which are types of quartz (KWAWRTS), are called semiprecious gemstones. The oldest known use of gemstones dates back about 20,000 years. Jade was carved in China 4,500 years ago. Diamonds were a source of Indian wealth 2,000 years ago.

Gemstones are minerals and are usually made of a number of chemical elements joined together. Some, such as gold and diamond, are single elements. Other materials, such as amber and pearls, are organic materials used as gems. Gemstones are often carved and cut into special shapes to improve their appearance.

Gemstones have always been associated with magic and folklore. The Persians thought that rubies were the source of power. Some people today believe that certain gems can heal illness.

The red ruby gemstone on the right has been cut from the rough mineral on the left. It has then been shaped and polished.

HIGHLIGHTS

- According to their value, gemstones may be precious or semiprecious.

- Gemstones can be identified by properties such as color, hardness, and luster.

- Gemstones occur in many parts of the world.

There are a number of ways gemstones can be identified, including the color, luster (LUHS-tuhr; reflective quality), hardness, specific gravity, and cleavage of the gemstone. Many gemstones have amazing colors. Ruby is a rich red color, and sapphire, which is chemically the same as ruby (both being forms of the mineral corundum), may be various shades of blue. Emerald is green and amethyst is purple. These colors are caused by the way in which light is reflected from the surface of the mineral or absorbed inside the crystal. Impurities in the mineral will also give the gem striking colors. Some gemstones are transparent (see-through) while others are translucent and let light pass into them. Heating or irradiating (exposing to radiation) a gemstone may change its color. Pink topaz can be made by heating brown specimens. Amethyst can be changed from purple to yellow by heating or radiation.

The way in which a gemstone's surface reflects light is called its luster. Some gemstones, such as amethyst, are very glassy, while others, including turquoise, are waxy. Some gemstones have small particles of fibrous mineral inside them, which causes a silky sheen within the gem. The sheen may be similar to a cat's eye or a star.

Topaz can occur in many different colors. Clear or finely colored varieties are used as gemstones.

Hardness is important because gemstones should be resistant to being scratched. A 10-point scale of mineral hardness was set up in 1812 by German scientist Friedrich Mohs (1773–1839). On this scale, talc is the softest and diamond the hardest. Most gemstones are above 7 but a few, such as green malachite (3.5 to 4 on the scale), are quite soft.

Specific gravity is the weight of the gemstone compared with the weight of an equal volume of water. Water has, by definition, a specific gravity of one. Diamond has a specific gravity of 3.52, ruby is 4.1, and amethyst is 2.65.

Minerals and gemstones break or cleave along lines of weakness related to their atomic structure. If this breaking can be repeated and produces the same shapes it is called cleavage. Some gems, such as topaz, cleave very well. Others such as amethyst have an atomic structure that is so strong they do not cleave. They simply fracture in an irregular way.

Crystals

Most gemstones occur naturally as crystals. A crystal has symmetry, which means that it looks the same from different directions. The many different crystal shapes are placed in six groups, called crystal systems. The cubic system is the most symmetrical. A cube looks the same from all sides. A less symmetrical but common system is the hexagonal. This system has six-sided crystals that often end in pointed pyramids.

Cutting and polishing

Someone who cuts and polishes gems is called a lapidary. He or she is able to make a sparkling gem from a dull, rough mineral. There are a number of well-known ways to shape gemstones. A cabochon is a gem with one rounded and one flat surface. Cabochons are often used to make rings and pendants. First the roughly shaped stone is stuck with wax onto the end of a small wooden stick. The stone is then held against a rotating abrasive wheel to produce the smooth shape. Faceted cuts are those used in transparent stones. The many smooth, cut faces on these stones act like mirrors, which make the gem sparkle. Diamonds are often faceted in a so-called brilliant cut, which can have as many as 58 faces. Today, the rough gem can be secured in a machine that is programmed to perfectly cut all the angles.

Many people cut and polish gems as a hobby. One of the simplest ways it to put the rough gemstones in a tumbling machine. The gemstones and a mixture of abrasive powder and water are placed in a small cylinder, which is rotated by the machine for about a week until the gems are highly polished.

Where gemstones are found

Gemstones are found all over the world, but certain countries have more than others. Brazil is famous for many types of gemstones, including diamond and emerald. In South Africa there are three deep diamond mines. Australia is well known for opals, and Columbia for emeralds. In India and Pakistan there are great quantities of ruby, sapphire, and topaz. Europe is not the best area for good gemstones. Topaz and amethyst are found in Germany. The United States is well known for its ruby and sapphire deposits. Russia has rich deposits of diamond, topaz, emerald, malachite, and garnet. Because gemstones are very resistant to erosion, they often occur in sand and gravel deposited by rivers. These gravels are worked by hand and by mechanical excavators. Some gems, such as the diamonds in South Africa, are mined deep underground. The Kimberlite mines, for example, are nearly a mile deep. Here 110 tons (100 tonnes) of rock produce just ½ oz (5 g) of diamond.

CHECK THESE OUT!
✔CRYSTAL ✔MINERALOGY ✔MINING

Geography

The scientific study of Earth's surface and related features

The word *geography* comes from ancient Greek and means "a picture or description of Earth." As long ago as the 6th century B.C.E., the Greeks began to describe and analyze the world around them. Since that time, geography has developed into a complex science. Physical geographers study landforms, soil science, and the behavior of the oceans, climate, and weather. Biogeographers study the distribution of living organisms around the world and their relation with the environment. Human geographers look at how the structure of Earth affects human cultures, activities, and organizations. All geography looks at where things are and why they are there.

HIGHLIGHTS

◆ Modern geographical studies include physical geography, biogeography, and social geography.

◆ Geographers need an understanding of other modern sciences, such as geology and chemistry.

History of geography

About 2,000 years ago, the ancient Greeks made observations of the stars and planets, winds, weather, and eclipses and analyzed them mathematically. As they studied the nature of Earth, they concluded it was a sphere. In about 200 B.C.E., Eratosthenes (around 276–194 B.C.E.) calculated Earth's circumference (the distance around the widest part of the world) using a branch of mathematics called geometry. His figure was approximately 25,000 miles. Today's figure for the circumference of the equator is 24,902 miles. Eratosthenes also wrote a work called *Geographica*, a history of what had so far been discovered about the world.

Strabo, a Greek scholar born in 63 B.C.E., produced a later work that defined the science of geography. In the 2nd century C.E., Greek geographer Ptolemy (100–170 C.E.) wrote *Geographia*, the most important writing on geography and mapmaking for the next 1,000 years.

Ptolemy also calculated the circumference of Earth but made it smaller than Eratosthenes. When the explorer Christopher Columbus (1451–1506) set out on his first voyage in 1492, he used Ptolemy's calculations. He expected to reach Asia by sailing from Spain to the west. Instead, however, he discovered the Caribbean islands. Columbus's voyages and discoveries encouraged further exploration, and maps became very important.

In 1595, an atlas of the discovered world was published. It was drawn by Flemish mapmaker Gerhard Kremer (1512–1594), known by the Latin version of his name, Gerardus Mercator. It included a description of how to draw lands and distances to scale, called the Mercator projection, which is still used for many maps.

Modern physical geography began with German naturalist and explorer Alexander von Humboldt (1769–1859). His name has been given to a number of Earth's physical phenomena, including the Humboldt Current, which runs northward along the coast of Peru.

Modern geography

As explorers found new lands, geographers concentrated on collecting descriptions of them. Their calculations relied mainly on astronomy and math. Modern geography makes use of methods from all branches of science. Physical geographers who study the world's atmosphere must know the latest discoveries and theories in physics and chemistry.

A portrait of Greek astronomer Claudius Ptolemy.

This map shows the height of Earth's surface as it would appear without the seas and oceans.

Geographers concerned with landmasses need a knowledge of science to understand changes produced by heat, cold, water, and atmospheric gases. Biogeographers must understand biology and ecology (the interrelationships of organisms and their surroundings).

Mapmaking

The surface of Earth is curved, but most maps must be drawn to be printed on a flat surface. The method used is called projection. There are many different types of projection, depending on the information that is given.

If the region represented by the map is small, projected distances and areas of land are fairly accurate. Projections of larger areas, such as maps of the world, are distorted. Only a spherical globe can show the correct surface of Earth. On a globe the parallels (lines of latitude, running east to west) are perpendicular (at right angles) to the meridians (muh-RIH-dee-uhnz; lines of longitude, running north to south). The meridians are all of the same length and meet at the North and South Poles.

When Mercator drew his maps, he was particularly concerned with navigation by sailors. A straight line drawn in any direction on a Mercator projection is a true compass bearing. Mercator's calculations made all the lines of both longitude and latitude parallel and the same length. Although maps are still published today with this projection, the distortion can be great.

Today a number of different projections are used. A conic projection imagines a cone set over an area of the globe, with that area projected onto the cone. Lines of longitude are straight lines radiating from a pole, and lines of latitude are curved. Goode's projection looks like a world map that has been peeled from a globe in sections. Robinson's projection is extensively used in popular atlases. It is highly appropriate for classroom use because it generally preserves the shapes and true areas of landmasses.

CHECK THESE OUT!
✔CLIMATE ✔EARTH ✔GEOLOGY ✔HYDROLOGY
✔LANDFORM ✔MAPS AND MAPPING
✔METEOROLOGY ✔OCEANOGRAPHY

Geologic Timescale

Chronological list of the rocks of Earth's crust

HIGHLIGHTS

◆ The geologic timescale covers the 4.6 billion years since Earth was formed.

◆ The history of Earth is subdivided by a variety of methods but especially by fossils.

◆ The end of the various major phases of Earth's history are marked by major environmental changes and extinction events.

The 4.6-billion-year history of Earth has been broken by many large-scale events that have left their mark on the environments and life of the time. Changes in the order of rock strata (STRAH-tuh; layers) and in the fossils (preserved remains) they contain show these events.

As geologists discovered the changes in rock strata in the 19th century they grouped similar fossils and strata into periods of geologic time, such as the Cambrian period or the Jurassic period. To begin with, the geologists did not have any method of dating strata in years. British geologist Charles Lyell (1797–1875) estimated that Earth was about 100 million years old. He based his measure on the thickness of known strata and on very rough estimates of

how long it took to deposit them. It was not until the beginning of the 20th century that the much more accurate radiometric dating of certain kinds of rocks allowed geologists to date the origin of rocks in years before the present. Radiometric

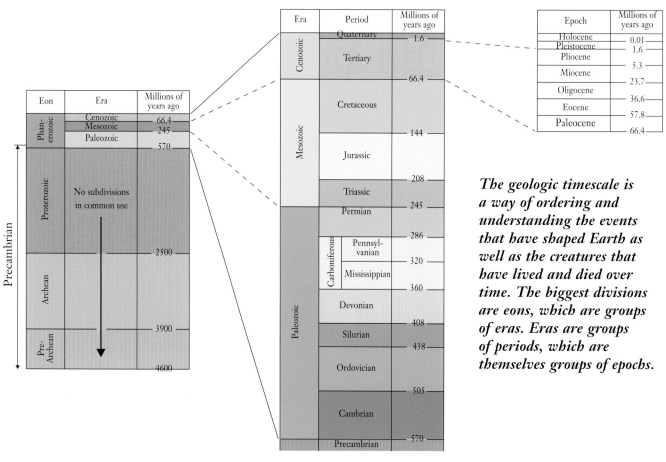

The geologic timescale is a way of ordering and understanding the events that have shaped Earth as well as the creatures that have lived and died over time. The biggest divisions are eons, which are groups of eras. Eras are groups of periods, which are themselves groups of epochs.

dating measures how long a radioactive element in the rocks has been giving off rays. This information tells geologists the age of that rock.

Dividing time

Geologists first began to map out the order of rock strata at the beginning of the 19th century. They discovered that particular types of fossils were found in different strata. Consequently, there was a recognizable pattern of changing fossils through time. Certain groups of fossils appeared in some layers of strata and then disappeared. For example, trilobites (TRY-luh-BYTS; ancient marine animals) were found only in ancient strata, and ammonites (A-muh-NYTS; ancient spiral-shelled animals) in younger strata. Fossils could be used to place particular strata in the overall arrangement of rocks through time.

During the 19th century, geologic time was divided into 11 periods, each characterized by particular fossils and representing particular phases of Earth's environmental history. The oldest period of time with a well-preserved record of shelly fossils is the Cambrian, which took place around 570 million to 505 million years ago. More recently, fossils have been found in Precambrian strata (dating from more than 570 million years ago).

The geologic periods are grouped into three eras: the Paleozoic (PAY-lee-uh-ZOH-ik), Mesozoic (MEH-zuh-ZOH-ik), and Cenozoic (SEE-nuh-ZOH-ik), which reflect major phases in Earth's history. The era boundaries are marked by major extinction events, when huge numbers of species (types) of living organisms died out. The trilobites became extinct at the end of the Paleozoic. The ammonites and dinosaurs became extinct at the end of the Mesozoic. Geologic periods are further subdivided into epochs (EH-puhks) and stages.

Radiometric dating

In 1897, Irish physicist Lord Kelvin (1824–1907) worked out that it took 20 to 40 million years for Earth to cool from a molten (liquid) state to its present temperature. His calculation was far too small. At the beginning of the 20th century, Arthur Holmes (1890–1965) in England and Bertram Boltwood (1870–1927) in the United States realized that the radioactive decay of chemical elements could be used to date the origin of minerals and the rocks that contained them. It became obvious that Earth was hundreds of millions of years old. The 4.6-billion-year age of Earth is based on dating meteorites, formed at the same time as Earth. Radiometric dating of minerals in rocks is best applied to granite (GRAH-nuht) and basalt lava (LAH-vuh), which were once molten and so formed at a fixed time.

CHECK THESE OUT!
✔EARTH ✔GEOLOGY ✔IGNEOUS ROCK ✔MAGMA

DISCOVERERS

William Smith

English surveyor William Smith (1769–1839) was one of the first people to study the layering of rock strata and their fossils. While working as a canal engineer, Smith realized that in any pile of strata, the higher layers are younger than the lower layers, and therefore their fossils are younger. From his observations of the strata and their fossils, Smith was able to build a column that showed the arrangement of the rock layers. Smith also made one of the earliest geological maps and vertical sections of the strata of entire countries when he published his map of England and Wales in 1815. Smith realized that if strata far apart contained the same index fossil, then the rocks were the same age. At about the same time, French geologists Georges Cuvier (1769–1832) and Alexandre Brongniart (1770–1847) independently discovered the same principles and made a geological map of the Paris region.

William Smith noticed the importance of rock layers.

Geology

The science of geology examines the rocks and the minerals from which they are made. Geologists also study fossils (FAH-sulz; preserved evidence of past life), which tell them about evolution, and materials in Earth's crust that are used as fuels or ores (sources of metals). Earth is an active planet and its rocks are always changing. Volcanoes, for example, make new rocks, and earthquakes break Earth's crust.

The study of geology

Serious study of rocks began in the 17th century. Much of the investigation of rocks was based on experience gained from mining and quarrying for coal and metals. In the 18th and 19th centuries, theory and practice began to come together. Investigating the rocks, their structure, and their fossils became a science.

Mapping methods developed, and scientists made detailed descriptions of the rocks and fossils. French geologist Baron Georges Cuvier (1769–1832) led the way in understanding fossil remains. William Smith (1769–1839) changed the understanding of the relative age of strata (STRAH-tuh; rock layers). He realized that each layer of rock was formed at a certain time. Fossils present in rocks were the remains of creatures that lived at that time. The oldest layers lay at the bottom. He was able to build a sequence of rock layers, each with its own typical fossils.

HIGHLIGHTS

◆ Humans have always needed rocks and metals from Earth. The ancient Greeks were the first to study geology.

◆ The study of geology as a science followed the mining and quarrying of rocks and ores.

◆ During the 19th century, geological research and mapping began. Geology became an accepted science in universities at around the same time.

Geological time

Geological time is studied in two different ways; one uses relative time and the other absolute time. Early scientists such as William Smith considered relative time. They subdivided the layers of rocks into time periods. Each period had its typical rocks and fossils. British professor Adam Sedgwick (1785–1873) named the first period the Cambrian period (570 million to 505 million years ago).

Using the principle that the oldest rocks are at the bottom, other younger time periods were established to account for all the layers. The Ordovician period (505 million to 438 million years ago) came after the Cambrian. Ordovician rocks lie on top of the Cambrian strata. Fossils of more advanced creatures occurred in the relatively younger rocks.

This valley is typical of one formed by a glacier—it has steep sides and a flat bottom. These are the sorts of clues put together by geologists as they study Earth.

The true age of Earth became known only after British physicist Ernest Rutherford (1871–1937) realized the importance of radioactivity. Earth contains many radioactive elements (substances with one basic kind of atom) that slowly decay into other materials. By studying this change, it is possible to calculate how long they have been decaying. This study reveals that Earth is 4.6 billion years old.

Many minerals and rocks contain radioactive (able to give off rays) elements. These decay over time into other elements. The speed at which half of the amount of a radioactive element change from parent (the original element) to daughter (the new element) takes place can be worked out, and is called the half-life. By very detailed analysis of rock samples, the amounts of parent and daughter elements now in the rock can be measured. By using the half-life of each element, the time it has taken to produce these amounts is calculated. This is the age of that rock sample. By using thousands of samples, a whole absolute timescale has been established, with numbers of millions of years placed beside the names of the time periods calculated by the early scientists.

STORY OF SCIENCE

The Ice Age and Changing Climates

Changes in Earth's climate are well known. The most recent ice age, which ended only 10,000 years ago, caused great changes to the landscape. In the middle of the 19th century, geologists tried to understand how Earth's surface was shaped by erosion and weathering. Scottish geologist Charles Lyell (1797–1875) and others were puzzled by the great, deep valleys in Scotland, Wales, and the Lake District of England. These features did not seem to be the work of rivers. Swiss-American scientist Louis Agassiz (1807–1873) visited Scotland in 1840 with William Buckland (1784–1856), an English geologist. Agassiz proved, by comparing the shape of these valleys with those in Switzerland, that they had been formed by glaciers and therefore that Britain had had glaciers.

Other studies

The wide subject of geology has many parts. Petrology, for example, is the study of rocks. The three main types of rocks, igneous (IG-nee-uhs), metamorphic (MEH-tuh-MAWR-fik), and sedimentary (SEH-duh-MEN-tuh-ree), and the way in which they form are investigated. Mineralogy is the study of the minerals that make up rocks. Minerals are identified according to their hardness, color, and chemical properties.

Geophysics looks at the way the rocks and Earth behave when under stresses caused by earthquakes. Geochemistry is the study of the elements in the rocks, soil, and water. Paleontology (PAY-lee-AHN-TAH-luh-jee) is the study of fossils, through which the evolution of life on Earth is understood. Stratigraphy is the science that puts all the geological events into the correct order on the timescale.

Much of geology is based on fieldwork and mapping. Through these techniques, geologists are able to predict how rocks behave below the ground and where important ores in rocks or in mineral deposits may be found.

CHECK THESE OUT!

✔EARTH ✔FOSSIL ✔GEOLOGIC TIMESCALE
✔MINERALOGY ✔PLATE TECTONICS ✔ROCK

Geyser

**Hot spring that suddenly shoots
a jet of water and steam into the air**

Hot springs that behave somewhat like volcanoes are called geysers (GY-zuhrz). From time to time, often with great regularity, they spout a fountain of boiling water and steam high in the air. Geysers have been known to spout water as high as 1,650 feet (500 m) in the air, but jets of 165 feet (50 m) are more common.

Geysers are found in regions of volcanic activity. Spectacular geysers are found in Yellowstone Park in Wyoming and also in New Zealand and Iceland. The word *geyser* is taken from the Icelandic verb *geysir*, which means "to rush forth." Geysir is also the name for one of the most famous geysers in Iceland.

How geysers work

Geysers are rare. They can occur only where three things are present: a supply of underground water, heat caused by volcanic activity or other heat sources deep within Earth, and a particular rock formation. Geysers happen where a hollow channel in the rock leads from deep underground to the surface. Some geyser tubes reach 330 feet

In Iceland and New Zealand, the steam from geysers is used to generate geothermal power. This is an economical but rather difficult process.

(100 m) below the surface. Groundwater (water within the earth that supplies wells and springs) collects in the tube and finally shoots upward through it. Some geysers also have a large chamber below ground in which water collects.

Surface rainwater seeps into the ground through cracks in the rocks and collects in the geyser tube to form a column of water. Deep underground, hot rocks heat the water to high temperatures. The tall column of water presses down on the lowest water, which is also the hottest. The water under pressure at the bottom of the tube becomes superheated—heated beyond the ordinary boiling point of water.

As the column of water heats up still more, water in the top part of the tube boils, expands, and is pushed up onto the surface. The water at the bottom is no longer under pressure and so it boils, shooting up the tube to erupt in a violent jet of liquid and steam. Hot springs and bubbling mud pots are often found near geysers and are much more common. They only need a supply of water to be warmed by hot rocks underground.

HIGHLIGHTS

◆ A geyser is a hot spring that erupts a jet of boiling water and steam from time to time.

◆ Geysers are rare. A supply of underground water, heat, and a hollow channel in the rock are all needed for a geyser to occur.

◆ A geyser erupts when a sudden drop in pressure inside the geyser tube causes the water at the bottom to boil and shoot up to the surface.

◆ The steam produced by geysers can be used to generate electricity.

Geysers behave in different ways. Some erupt for a few minutes and then go quiet for hours or even days. Others erupt more regularly. Geysers that erupt regularly are supplied with a steady trickle of groundwater that takes a set time to fill the tube or chamber. The time between each eruption, therefore, is almost the same.

Over time, geysers can be affected by rock movements caused by earthquakes. Geysir, the famous geyser in Iceland, has been fairly quiet since 1916. It now spouts much less often than other geysers in the area, such as Strokur, which erupts every few minutes. In Yellowstone National Park, the earthquake of 1959 caused several hot springs to become new geysers.

Investigating geysers

Scientists are still working out the mysteries of geysers. From 1992 to 1993, scientists at Yellowstone National Park lowered a research probe containing a tiny video camera into the mouth of the famous geyser, Old Faithful.

Working between eruptions, the scientists videoed the scene inside the geyser tube and measured water temperatures. At a depth of 45 feet (13 m), the camera recorded a seething liquid tornado of swirling, superheated water. The water temperature deep below ground was well above the temperature at which water boils at the surface, because under pressure water can reach a higher temperature without boiling.

Inside a geyser's tube the superheated water dissolves some of the minerals in the rocks. Water from geysers is often rich in the minerals silica or calcium. When they reach the surface, these minerals precipitate (solidify) to form small mounds of white or gray material around the geyser's mouth. Calcium may be deposited in the form of mounds or terraces. Hot springs also contain large amounts of sulfur.

Electricity from geysers

The steam from geysers can be harnessed to generate electricity. Electricity made in this way is cheaper than electricity generated in the usual way by burning fossil fuels such as oil and gas.

However, it is not easy to harness geysers. The generating stations need to be carefully maintained because the dissolved chemicals in

LOOK CLOSER

Old Faithful

Old Faithful in Yellowstone National Park is one of the world's most famous geysers. It erupts for a few minutes about once every 65 minutes. While most geysers do not erupt so regularly, the time periods between Old Faithful's eruptions have changed little in the last 100 years. Even for Old Faithful, however, the intervals between eruptions can vary by up to 25 percent.

Since records of its activity began, Old Faithful has never missed an eruption. It regularly spouts a jet of boiling water to heights of 100 to 170 feet (30 to 52 m), blowing out about 10,000 gallons (38,000 l) of water with each eruption.

the steam are very corrosive and quickly destroy metal parts. The steam also deposits minerals inside the station's pipes, which can quickly clog and become useless.

CHECK THESE OUT!
✔EVAPORATION AND BOILING
✔GROUNDWATER ✔HEAT

Glacier

Enormous masses of land ice made of packed-down and recrystallized snow are called glaciers (GLAY-shurz). Glaciers appear motionless but are moving masses of ice. They flow slowly downhill, carrying rock fragments and sometimes huge boulders with them.

Glaciers cover about 10 percent of Earth's surface. They contain about 75 percent of all the fresh water on Earth, locked up in the form of ice. Today's glaciers are found only in cold places such as the polar and subpolar regions, and high in mountainous areas nearer to the equator (ih-KWAY-tuhr; imaginary circle around Earth at equal distances from the North and South Poles). About 95 percent of Earth's glaciers are found on the huge, icy continent of Antarctica in the far south and on the large island of Greenland in the far north. Greenland is the only large landmass in the Arctic, which is mostly a huge, ice-covered ocean, so there are fewer glaciers in the far north than in the far south.

At various times during Earth's long history, the world's climate was much colder than it is today. During long, cold periods called ice ages, ice covered up to a quarter of Earth's land surface, and glaciers flowed over much of Europe and North America. As Earth's climate grew warmer around 10,000 years ago, the ice sheets melted and the glaciers retreated. Scientists now know that during prehistory, ice sheets advanced and retreated over Earth's surface many times.

How glaciers form

Glaciers form only in certain conditions. They develop only in cold places where most of the precipitation (moisture) that falls each year falls as snow. In such cold places, not all the snow is melted by the Sun's rays during the warmer months of the year. Instead, it gradually builds up to form a large mass. As fresh falls of snow press down on the layers beneath, the snow crystallizes and turns to ice. Gradually a hard,

HIGHLIGHTS

♦ Glaciers flow very slowly downhill, carrying rock fragments embedded in the ice.

♦ Glaciers now cover about 10 percent of Earth's surface. They are found in polar and subpolar regions and high in mountains elsewhere.

♦ During past ice ages, glaciers covered much more of Earth's surface than they do today.

heavy, solid mass of ice is formed. When the mass of ice grows large enough, its own enormous weight sets it moving downhill.

The source of the glacier, where fresh snow falls, is called the head. It may be high up in the mountains or inland in the far north or south of Earth. From the snout (the downslope end), the ice in a glacier flows downhill. At the terminus (foot), the ice may melt due to the warmer temperatures that occur, such as on the lower mountain slopes. In the polar regions, ice flows slowly from the center of the land toward the sea. At the coast, the edge of the ice breaks off to form icebergs or floating ice shelves in the water.

Types of glaciers

There are two main glacier shapes: dome-shaped and channel (or valley) glaciers. Dome-shaped glaciers spread out in all directions to cover a wide area. Channel glaciers flow down narrow valleys between mountain ridges. They cannot spread sideways because they are hemmed in by ridges of high ground on either side.

Dome-shaped glaciers include the massive ice sheets of Antarctica, Greenland, and Iceland, which are the size of continents. Dome glaciers are also found on the summits of flat-topped mountains. In most dome-shaped glaciers, the ice dome covers the high ground at the center of the

LOOK CLOSER

Glacial Erosion

In mountain regions, erosion by glaciers causes striking landscape features. Deep, U-shaped valleys are formed by fast-moving glaciers. Hanging valleys are side valleys that enter the main valley high above the central U-shaped channel. They are caused by smaller, slow-moving glaciers. High, sharp peaks and narrow mountain ridges called arêtes may be carved by two or more glaciers. Fjords are valleys originally cut by glaciers, now flooded by the sea.

glacier. Around the edges, tongue-shaped glaciers fan out and drain into the surrounding lowlands. Rocky outcrops called nunataks sometimes stick up through the ice.

Channel glaciers include trough glaciers, which are long, narrow glaciers flowing in valleys between mountains. They also include smaller masses of ice that build up in cirques (SUHRKS), or steep-sided, bowl-shaped hollows in the mountains. Cirque glaciers develop in areas where there is not enough snow to force the ice

The Athabasca glacier is a frozen river in Alberta, Canada. It forms part of the Columbia Icefield.

The top of this glacier has cracked into spires of ice. These spires form when different parts of the glacier move at different speeds and break apart.

to move downhill. Where a channel glacier flows out of its confining mountain walls, the ice spreads to form a fan or semicircle.

How glaciers move

Glacier ice flows because of the force of gravity. If the surface on which the ice rested did not slope, the glacier would not move. In mountain regions, glacier ice travels up to 3 feet (1 m) a day. Polar glaciers flow more slowly.

Glaciers move by shearing internally or sliding along the bedrock. Both polar and mountain glaciers experience shearing, but only warm mountain glaciers slide along their base. Shearing happens when the huge weight of the ice pressing down causes the ice inside the glacier to shear, or break apart. Large vertical cracks called crevasses form deep in the ice and stretch up to the surface. At the surface, crevasses are a great danger to travelers and mountaineers.

Glaciers and erosion

Erosion is the wearing away of the land by natural forces such as ice. Glaciers are important causes of erosion. They wear down Earth's surface in several different ways. The weight of

the ice pressing down on the bedrock below causes the rocks to crack and break. The broken pieces of rock then become embedded in the underside of the glacier and are carried along. In turn, these rock pieces speed up the process of erosion by scouring, scratching, or grinding against the surface rock. The melted water beneath the glacier seeps into cracks in the rock. There it freezes again and expands, widening the cracks until the rock splits open.

Glaciers act as giant conveyer belts carrying large quantities of broken rock. The rock debris (duh-BREE), called moraine, varies in size from fine dust to giant boulders. Much of this material is embedded in the glacier's base, but rock fragments are also carried on top, at the sides, and in front of the glacier. Eventually, the material is deposited in heaps at the foot of the glacier as the ice melts. These heaps are called terminal moraines. The material may be deposited to form long, egg-shaped hills called drumlins, or narrow, straight ridges called flutes.

CHECK THESE OUT!
✔EROSION ✔GLOBAL WARMING ✔ICE AGE
✔RAIN, SLEET, AND SNOW ✔RIVER ✔VALLEY

THE FUTURE

Glaciers and Global Warming

At present, the world's glaciers are retreating as the result of a natural warming of Earth's climate over the last 10,000 years. Recently, scientists have become concerned that human activities such as the burning of fossil fuels are speeding up this natural warming process, called global warming. If global warming continues to accelerate, Earth's glaciers will melt, causing sea levels to rise around the world. This rise in sea levels would lead to widespread flooding in low-lying areas, particularly near sea coasts. Recently, representatives from many nations have met to try to reach agreement about the best ways to tackle the problem of global warming.

Global Warming

The gradual and continual increase in Earth's air temperature

Many people believe that Earth's climate is about to change dramatically. The changes may be the most extreme the world has experienced for 10,000 years. There is evidence that the average annual temperature of the air is increasing. This global warming is apparently due to human activities and way of life.

The greenhouse effect

Life on Earth depends on the energy of the Sun. The Sun radiates visible light, which causes plants to grow, and so begins the food chain. The Sun also radiates ultraviolet (UV) energy, much of which is reflected by Earth's ozone layer. Much of the UV and visible light energy striking Earth's surface is changed to heat energy. Earth then radiates this heat as infrared (IR) energy. Some IR escapes into space, but much is absorbed by the atmosphere. In this way, the air is warmed to an average annual temperature of

HIGHLIGHTS

◆ Greenhouse gases absorb infrared energy radiated by Earth, which warms up the atmosphere.

◆ The main natural greenhouse gases are water vapor, carbon dioxide, methane, and nitrous oxide.

◆ Clouds help to keep Earth cool.

◆ Scientists use computer models to help predict future climate changes.

59°F (33°C). This natural phenomenon is called the greenhouse effect. Without it the air would be too cold to support life on Earth.

The main natural gases (the greenhouse gases) in the atmosphere that absorb IR are water vapor, carbon dioxide, methane, and nitrous oxide. For thousands of years, the levels of these gases remained fairly constant. During the last 200 years they have risen dramatically due to changes in the way people live. As a result, the atmosphere will absorb more IR energy and its temperature will probably continue to rise.

Water vapor is the most important absorber of IR. Changes in its level generally take place in a local way. When tropical forests are cut down for logging, the water vapor level is decreased in that area. Levels of other greenhouse gases are increasing, due to modern-day human activities. Carbon dioxide is produced by the burning of fossil fuels such as coal, oil, and natural gas. When forests are cleared and burned so that the land can be cultivated, more carbon dioxide is released. Levels of the gas have risen by 30 percent in the last 200 years, by 25 percent in the 20th century, and by 10 percent during

Car fumes contain two of the main greenhouse gases: nitrous oxide and carbon dioxide. Many cars are now fitted with catalytic converters, which change harmful gases into mostly harmless products.

313

the last 30 years. Livestock, rice paddies, landfills, and pipeline leaks release methane. Nitrous oxide is produced in automobile exhausts.

Particular concern has been caused by the escape of chlorofluorocarbons (CFCs) into the atmosphere, which contribute to the greenhouse effect and disturb the ozone layer. These gases are completely human-made and have been used in refrigerators, as solvents, and as propellants in aerosol sprays. However, recent legislation has restricted their manufacture and use, and safe substitutes are being found for them.

Studying climate changes

The way that radiation of heat from Earth affects the atmosphere's temperature is complicated. Predicting how the world climate may change in the future is also difficult. Scientists measure the composition of the atmosphere and attempt to forecast what will happen. They also make computer simulations called General Circulation Models (GCMs), which can be used to ask questions. Observations show that the levels of greenhouse gases are increasing. GCMs forecast that this increase will lead to global warming.

Terraced and flooded rice paddies like these in Bali, Indonesia, are used for growing rice. Rice paddies release methane, a greenhouse gas.

GCMs are the closest thing to a twin Earth, but the calculations used to build them is much simpler than the real state of affairs. Scientists feed the data from their observations into the GCM calculations. Then they fast-forward the time and find out what the GCM predicts about future atmospheric changes. What if the level of carbon dioxide in the atmosphere increases at its present rate until it doubles? The GCMs reveal that Earth's average annual air temperature will rise by 2.7°F to 9.9°F (1.5°C to 5.5°C).

These figures show that it is difficult for GCMs to make very accurate predictions. It might seem that a good way to test the models would be to look at the records of climate changes that have been kept in the past. This is not easy, however. Temperature records have been made at many sites around the world during the last 100 years. There is some evidence of global warming, but many temperature rises are not due to changes in the greenhouse effect.

Some sites at which temperatures are measured have been moved. Other sites have been added, mainly in hotter parts of the world. Cities have grown quickly around these observation sites, making local hot spots.

However, scientists have found a different way to discover the composition of the atmosphere, in climates from as long ago as 200,000 years. As ice sheets grew and spread at the North and South Poles, they trapped pockets of air. Taking samples of ice, the scientists can release the air and analyze the levels of the different greenhouse gases in the atmosphere when the air was trapped. They have found that changes in carbon dioxide levels often coincided with variations in global temperature.

Earth's climate naturally changes from year to year. Locally—and even on a global scale—there are hot years and cold years, dry years and wet years. This can be due to eruptions of volcanoes, shifting plates in Earth's crust, and even variations in the Sun's electrical activity. However, these changes do not seem to account for all the present gradual global warming.

The planet heats up

Some computer calculations have suggested that the warming would not be the same all over the globe. It might be greater over land, particularly high up on the hills and mountains, at night, or during the winter. Many world communities

The Sun's rays pass through the outer layer of the atmosphere. Some are reflected back out to space by the clouds. The rest are absorbed by Earth's surface.

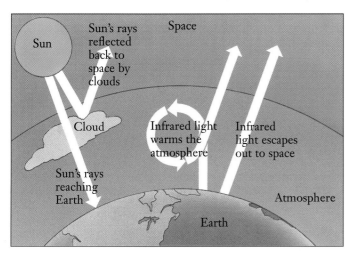

THE FUTURE

Reducing Global Warming

There are many ways in which the effects of global warming can be reduced. This would slow down climate changes. The speed with which the climate changes is as important as how much it changes.

What can be done? First, energy could be used more wisely. Homes could be fully insulated, and unnecessary use of electricity could be stopped. Cars could be used less often, and arrangements made to recycle all trash. Second, greater efforts could be made to keep Earth green. More trees could be planted, and governments and industries could be persuaded to reduce felling and burning forests.

would grow warmer, but some could become cooler. Overall, rainfall would probably increase due to the greater evaporation from warm seas. There would also be local droughts (periods of excessive dryness).

It is impossible to predict short-term changes in climate or future storms and other violent weather events. Some scientists predict, however, that the average sea level will rise 18 inches (46 cm) during the next 100 years. This will be due to the oceans warming up and expanding, and to glaciers and polar icecaps melting, so increasing the amount of water. Coastal communities and even inland town and city populations may have to spend a great deal of money to protect themselves against the rising water.

The situation may not be so bad as it seems. There are some atmospheric changes that are likely to lessen the greenhouse effect. For example, solid pollution particles in the air such as smoke and ash can reduce global warming. Water droplets form around them to become clouds, which reflect UV radiation back into space. Less UV radiation reaches Earth to warm it, and so Earth radiates less IR back into the atmosphere. Therefore, a cloudier Earth can be a cooler Earth.

CHECK THESE OUT!
✔ATMOSPHERE ✔CARBON DIOXIDE
✔CLIMATE ✔POLLUTION

Gold

A shiny, bright yellow metal used mainly for jewelry, electronics, and dentistry

One of the first elements to be known to humans, gold is one of the few that occur naturally as pure metals. Apart from copper, gold is the only metal that is not silvery white when pure. It has an attractive shiny yellow color and does not tarnish (become dull). Gold's rarity and beauty have made it a symbol of power and wealth since ancient civilizations.

Properties of gold

Gold is a soft metal and can be formed into different shapes more easily than other metals. It can be hammered to make a foil called gold leaf. It can also be drawn (pulled) to make fine wires. A single ounce of gold can be stretched to form an unbroken wire over 40 miles (64 km) long.

Gold's most notable chemical property is that it reacts with very few chemicals. While most metals form salts and dissolve with many strong acids, selenic acid is the only pure acid that can

Roughly 45 percent of all the gold in the world is held by governments and central banks.

HIGHLIGHTS

◆ Gold is very rare and occurs naturally as a pure metal in the ground.

◆ Highly valued for its beauty, gold is used to make coins, jewelry, and for other decorative effects.

◆ Gold is an extremely unreactive metal.

dissolve gold. Gold also dissolves in a mixture of hydrochloric and nitric acids called aqua regia, from the Latin words meaning "royal water."

Uses of gold

Gold, or a mixture of gold and other metals, is often used to make coins. Because of its attractive appearance, gold is also used to make jewelry and

STORY OF SCIENCE

The Gold Rush of 1849

In the 19th century, people in the United States, Canada, Australia, and South Africa flocked to the sites of newly discovered gold deposits. These were called gold rushes. In the winter of 1847 to 1848, German-born landowner John Augustus Sutter (1803–1890) was having a sawmill built on his land in Sacramento Valley, California. Carpenter James Marshall (1810–1885) found a nugget of gold as he was digging the foundations for the sawmill. When Marshall told his employer of the discovery, Sutter swore all to secrecy, hoping to stop others from taking the gold. News soon leaked, however, to store owner Samuel Brennan. He stocked his store with mining equipment and set about spreading the news

in San Francisco. Within days, thousands were flocking to Sacramento in search of gold. By that summer, word had spread along the West Coast and into Mexico. In December 1848, the discovery of gold was announced to the U.S. Congress. In 1849, the number of miners (called forty-niners) in Sacramento reached 80,000. This figure tripled within four years. Many miners worked in groups. Large mining companies started to move into Sacramento Valley. The easiest gold deposits had been stripped, and many self-employed miners found little or no gold. The companies were better equipped for mining in hard-to-reach deposits, and the forty-niners started to drift back to their old lives. Sutter lost his land to the crowds of miners and died bankrupt.

decorative objects. The metal's lack of chemical reactivity means its appearance is not spoiled by the formation of oxides or other compounds. Gold is normally used in alloys (metal mixtures) with copper or nickel, however, because it is expensive. As well as being cheaper than pure gold, alloys are harder and less prone to damage. The proportion of gold to other metals in an alloy is given in karats (KAR-uhts). Pure gold is 24 karat, 50 percent gold is 12 karat, and so on.

A way to reduce the amount of gold used to decorate objects is to apply a very fine film of gold. Gold leaf can be stuck to books using an adhesive (glue) such as egg white. Metal objects can be coated by applying a thin foil of gold and fixing it using pressure or heat. Electroplating applies a fine film of gold using electrical current.

Solid gold is useful where extremely low chemical reactivity is important. It is used for dental repairs and for making some artificial body parts. Its lack of reactivity also makes gold ideal for electrical contacts.

Sources of gold

Gold comes from fluids that rise through cracks in Earth's crust. When they cool, these fluids form veins (lodes) of gold mixed with quartz (KWAWRTS) and other minerals. In some cases, rain wears away the rock of a lode and washes gold nuggets (lumps) downstream, which settle on the beds of streams and rivers. This type of deposit is called a placer. South Africa, the United States, and Canada are the main gold producers. The Mother Lode in California was the scene of the Gold Rush of 1849 and has produced more gold than any other U.S. deposit.

Gold from mines and placers is purified by amalgamation (uh-mal-guh-MAY-shuhn). Gold-bearing ore is mixed with mercury, which dissolves gold from the ore. Mercury is then boiled out of the liquid amalgam to leave gold metal, which is further purified by electrolysis. Impure gold is made at the anode (positive terminal) in an electrolytic cell containing gold chloride and hydrochloric acid. Pure gold is deposited at the cathode (negative terminal).

CHECK THESE OUT!
✔ELECTROLYSIS ✔MERCURY ✔METAL

Gondwana

Geologists believe that up to 208 million years ago all the dry land on Earth was combined in one single huge continent, which was surrounded by ocean in the southern hemisphere. They call this supercontinent Pangaea, which means "all lands."

In the early 1900s, German meteorologist Alfred Wegener (1880–1930) pointed out that the shape of the present-day continents could be fitted together like the pieces of a giant jigsaw puzzle. He could not explain how these pieces broke apart, but geologists have now developed a theory called plate tectonics. Earth's crust, and a small part of the upper mantle, is made of large plates that are continually moving very slowly. These are called tectonic (tek-TAH-nik) plates. Gradually, the movement of these plates tore Pangaea into two roughly equal parts, which have been named Laurasia and Gondwana (which is sometimes called Gondwanaland).

Each supercontinent then began to be forced apart and split up even more. Laurasia moved northward and began to divide into the landmasses that today are North America, Europe, and Asia. Gondwana gradually divided into Africa, South America, Antarctica, Australia, and India. Around 135 million years ago, South America had begun to detach from the western edge of Africa. Antarctica and Australia were still joined together but had also separated from Africa. A smaller piece, which became India, broke away. It moved north and eventually collided with the southern edge of Asia. This collision produced the Himalaya Mountains, the highest on Earth.

This diagram shows the approximate shape of Gondwana and the positions of the modern-day continents that made up the supercontinent.

Today's geologists believe that Gondwana and Laurasia were separate supercontinents about 500 million years ago. This was early in the Paleozoic era, when the first land animals began to appear. Around 300 to 250 million years ago, Laurasia and Gondwana collided to form Pangaea. The force of the collision crumpled Earth's crust, forming mountains in many places.

The evidence

Scientists compare geological features, such as types of rocks and fossils, to figure out which present-day landmasses were connected. If similar features are found on two separate landmasses, this suggests they were once joined. Parts of Africa, South America, Australia, Asia, and Antarctica have deep grooves on their surfaces. They all seem to have been cut by glaciers at about the same time. In Africa there is evidence of glacial erosion, and these same glaciers left thick deposits of clay and boulders in what is now Brazil. This is striking evidence that the Atlantic Ocean did not exist at that time.

Fossilized plant and animal remains provide another clue. Land animals would not have been able to cross the deep ocean that separates Africa and Antarctica. So, if fossils from a particular time period are found in both continents, this shows they were joined at that time. Around 160 million years ago, a reptile rather similar to a hippopotamus existed. Its fossils have been found in South Africa, Antarctica, China, and India. This shows that, at that time, these regions were still connected, so this animal could roam freely across the land.

Africa

South America

India

Antarctica

Australia

CHECK THESE OUT!
✔CONTINENT
✔FOSSIL ✔PANGAEA
✔PLATE TECTONICS

Glossary

abrasive (uh-BRAY-siv) Substance used to smooth or polish another by rubbing or scraping.

altitude Height above sea level.

ancestor (AN-SEHS-tuhr) Individual who lived long before another member of the same family or species.

axle (AK-suhl) Rod through a wheel or pair of wheels, around which they rotate.

chain reaction Series of events where each one triggers the next.

extraterrestrial Not from Earth—often used to refer to possible life on other planets.

fertile Able to support life or produce offspring.

fibrous (FY-bruhs) Made of or resembling fibers (long, thin, threadlike structures).

fjord (fee-AWRD) Inlet of the sea between cliffs or steep slopes; formed by glacial erosion.

flare Blaze of light used as a signal or a warning. A solar flare is a sudden outburst of energy from the Sun's surface.

fungi (FUN-gee) Organisms that live on rotting matter. Molds, mushrooms, and yeast are fungi.

genus (JEE-nuhs) Group of closely related species that share certain characteristics.

gravitational slingshot Maneuver by a spacecraft as it uses a planet's gravity to speed up.

inversely proportional The relationship between two quantities, in which one gets bigger as the other gets smaller.

lubricate To make slippery by applying a substance such as oil (called a lubricant). This reduces friction between moving parts of machinery.

luster Shininess. A glow produced by reflected light.

meltdown The accidental melting of the core of a nuclear reactor.

meridian Imaginary circle on the surface of Earth that passes through the poles.

Middle East The countries of southwest Asia and northeast Africa, from Libya in the west to Afghanistan in the east.

mudflat Level area of land just covered by shallow water. Also, muddy land covered and uncovered by the tide.

North Star Also called *polestar*. The star in the Northern Hemisphere toward which Earth's imaginary axis points.

peninsula Piece of land jutting out into the water.

plate boundary Area where two plates of Earth's crust meet.

porous (PAWR-uhs) Full of pores (tiny channels). Water can seep into porous rock.

quark (KWAWRK) Subatomic particle thought to exist in pairs. *See also* subatomic particles.

quarrying (KWAH-ree-ing) Extracting useful material such as building stone from a site (called a quarry).

reservoir (REH-zuhr-vwahr) Stored supply, for example, of water. Often a humanmade lake.

saturate (SA-chuh-RAYT) To fill with a substance until no more can be taken in.

silicon chip Wafer of silicon that is the main part in an electric circuit.

species (SPEE-sheez) Type of organism able to interbreed.

subatomic particles Particles within an atom, including protons, electrons, and neutrons.

subduction zone Area where one plate of Earth's crust descends below another.

suborbital Not completing a full orbit; going only part way around an object.

superheated Liquid heated above its boiling point without it turning into a vapor (gas).

void (VOYD) Empty space.

Index

Page numbers in **boldface type** refer to main
articles and their illustrations. Page numbers
in *italic type* refer to additional illustrations.

550
EXP
#4

Exploring Earth and
Space Science

05/06	DATE DUE		

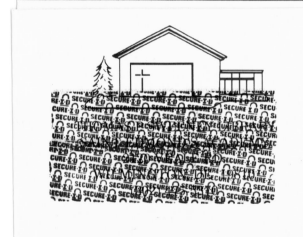